KING'S PLEASURE

Books *by* Ida Zeitlin

Illustrated by Theodore Nadejen

SKAZKI

GESSAR KHAN

KING'S PLEASURE

Illustrated by Theodore Nadejen

Oscar Wilde's FISHERMAN AND
HIS SOUL

KING'S PLEASURE

BY

IDA ZEITLIN

WITH ILLUSTRATIONS BY

THEODORE NADEJEN

HARPER & BROTHERS PUBLISHERS

NEW YORK AND LONDON

1929

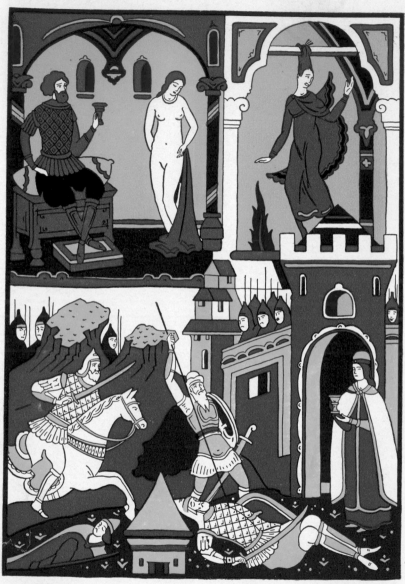

(See page 120)

TO HIS EXCELLENCY

JOHN DYNELEY PRINCE

MINISTER PLENIPOTENTIARY
FROM THE UNITED STATES
TO THE KINGDOM OF THE
SERBS, CROATS AND SLOVENES

FOREWORD

While the principal events of this story are grounded on a solid historical basis, I have used as the immediate source of my material, wherever possible, the legends woven by the Serbian people about these events rather than the record of more sober documents, with the result that kings drink wisdom from the lips of falcons, and the deities of wood and mountain interfere in matters that are commonly regarded as the business of the historian alone. My object has been to present a picture of the age, and I believe that this naïve blend of fact and fancy reflects its spirit more truly than any other method at my disposal.

The idea for the book was conceived by Mr. Theodore Nadejen, who visited the monasteries of Serbia to obtain much first-hand material that would not otherwise have been available.

IDA ZEITLIN

August 6, 1929

KING'S PLEASURE

"Let not the sorrows of this fair world oppress you."

—SAINT SAVA OF SERBIA

KING'S PLEASURE

ATHER about me, my children, and hearken unto the tale of your kings and your people, eagles who spread their wings from Pomorye to the shores of the Black Sea, and from our mother Danube to the proud-rising walls of Tsarigrad. Maimed is the eagle's wing, and his talons fettered, and he pines in bondage whom God made to fly free under His firmament. Yet hear and exult, ye eagles' brood, in the glory of your fathers! Hear and lament for the shining days that are done!

A time there was, beyond the memory of the ancient dead, when our people were folded in darkness, knowing naught of the world nor of God's covenant with man. But the Lord Who wished them well drew them across the waters of the Danube, revealing pleasant pastures for their flocks and fruitful earth for the planting of wheat and vineyards. And on the hills of high Illyria they lighted beacon-fires, that those who dwelt in the land might know of their coming, yet they molested none, but took up their abode in lonely places and herded their flocks and planted their fields and vineyards, and went freely as in the country of their birth. And having led them to their appointed place, God caused the undying flame of His truth to be kindled among them, scattering the darkness, and they bowed down before the Holy Cross.

Now they who named themselves lords over all this fair realm were the Grecian Tsars, yet for many long years they troubled us not, being deep in war with the heathen of far lands. Till at length one subdued his foe, and returning to Tsarigrad, sent his warriors to drive us again beyond the mighty stream whence we were come. But we stood firm against them, for we had learned the way of their warfare, and feared them not.

And when he saw that he might not work his will upon us by force of arms, the Tsar strove with smiling words to ensnare us, saying: "Do ye pay me tribute, ye Serbs, and as my vassals ye shall dwell forever in peace among us."

But our chieftains answered him: "While swords and battle endure, what man that breathes under the sunlight shall name us slaves?" And they girded their weapons upon them, and went forth to assail the foe, laying waste their citadels and seizing their store of silver and of gold. And this was done with God's blessing, for He was angered against the Greeks, who had forsaken holiness for evil ways, and dishonored the banner of Christ raised high by the hand of the blessèd Constantine. Treasure and boundless might

2

had He bestowed upon them, and dominion over many peoples, and the wondrous church of Saint Sofia like an angel in their midst. Yet they fell from His grace, giving ear to the voice of Satan, and those who were vowed to His service, yea, monk and nun, lay in sin together, and bishops strove with each other for sovereignty, profaning their Master's Word, and decked their feasts with the vessels wrought for His shrine. And harlots went arrayed in the robes of His virgins, and the charioteer was honored above the saint.

And Mihailo the Tsar led his people in wickedness, outdoing them as the wolf outdoes the swine, for he recked not the weal of his empire nor his soul, but his days were given to the pleasures of the chariot-race, and his nights to lechery, and the rich treasure garnered by his fathers he wasted in ill living. And he flouted the church, garbing his comrades in priestly vestments, and sending them forth to ride on asses through the streets of Tsarigrad and bow in mockery before the holy eikons; and when the Patriarch chided their blasphemy, they made answer with mirth and the singing of unclean songs.

And the Tsar knew not his wife, but Yevdokia, his leman, went ever by his side, and in the presence of all his court he lay with her, O shameless one! And he drank of the wine-cup not as men are wont to drink, savoring its joys, but without stint or measure, till his blood was inflamed and his follies defy the tongue to tell of them.

Yet folly of all his follies lay herein, that he exalted to the highest place Basil of Makedon, he who had

3

been a wrestler and keeper of steeds, but withal a man of might, burning for honors greater than he had won, yea, even for the glory of Cæsar's throne.

And that ye may know how this people had deserved God's malison, ye shall hear a tale of their revels and their bloody deeds.

In his Hall of Couches, Mihailo, Tsar of the Greeks, held festival amid such splendor as in visions ye may not behold. Of gleaming marble were the walls of his feasting-hall, and marble columns rose higher than the eye could follow them, and the floor was encrusted with many-colored jewels, and from crystal basins fountains flung aloft their silver crowns. And the air was sweet with the voice of lute and tambour, and bright with the flame of a thousand burning tapers, and on couches strewn with samite and cloth of gold Mihailo and his lords and courtesans drank and made merry. And Basil of Makedon lay at the Tsar's right hand, and Yevdokia, his leman, whom he had wedded to Basil, on his left. And fair youths and maidens went unclad among them as cupbearers.

Now Mihailo, having drunk deep, raised high his hand, and the music was stilled, and the laughter and lustful shouts, and the eyes of all were turned upon their sovereign.

And he cried: "My friends and comrades in joy, to-day we feast, but we shall fast on the morrow, for our coffers stand bare of gold. Now he who can teach me

4

how they should be filled again shall sit at my right hand, and be decked this night in the purple shoes of the Tsar."

And the brow of Basil grew dark, yet he dared speak no word to hinder his lord, and Liskyan the Wrestler arose and spoke, saying: "O thou born to the purple, the Arab merchants would buy of thee the wonders of Theophilus, thy father, the golden lions that roar beside the throne, the golden griffons, and the tree of gold, wherein mock birds make music sweeter than the song of the nightingale. And they will pay thee in such weight of treasure that thou shalt feast more bounteously in days to come than ever thou hast feasted."

Then Basil cried: "Heed not the counsel of Liskyan, I pray thee, sire, for thy people will clamor to know themselves bereft of these wonders."

But Mihailo answered: "What is their clamor to me? Let the merchants be summoned, and bring me hither the golden beasts of Theophilus, my father."

And when they had been brought, in truth, ye would have rejoiced to behold them. For the golden lions lifted up their heads and roared, and the golden griffons beat their mighty wings, and the leaves of the tree were stirred as by a gentle zephyr while golden birds made music in its branches sweeter than the song of the nightingale.

And Mihailo cried to the merchants: "What will ye give me, ye black-skinned dogs, for the pride of my palace?"

And they answered: "We will fill thy coffers with

5

gold to overflowing, and what they cannot hold, we will heap beside them to the doors of thy treasure-house." And the Tsar was content.

But when the merchants were departed, and the golden creatures of Theophilus borne away, gloom like an ebon pall descended on that company as though one had perished from their midst. Only Mihailo laughed aloud and said unto them: "Take heart, my tender doves! What hawk do ye fear? For these beasts of gold that roar and beat their wings and know naught beside, we will buy golden wine and golden steeds and golden maidens, to drain them of delight. Yea, richly hast thou earned thy guerdon, Liskyan the Wrestler. Come, draw from the feet of thy Tsar his purple shoes, and deck thine own."

And Liskyan would have done his bidding, but the eyes of Basil were fixed in such hatred upon him that his hand trembled, and he might not draw the shoe from his master's foot. And seeing his terror, Mihailo, ablaze with wine, turned upon Basil, crying: "Who art thou, scullion of the stables, to thwart my pleasure? Though of my graciousness I raised thee out of the slime to a place beside me, still I am Tsar and honor whom I will."

And Basil bowed low before him, answering naught, but Yevdokia, thinking to allay his wrath, laid her white arm about his neck and spoke softly, saying: "Thou art folded in glory, O Basileus, too radiant for mortals to look upon. Wilt thou cloud thy mantle to share it with a slave?"

But Mihailo flung her away, crying: "Is thy lord

6

who shares my mantle of prouder birth? Let him beware lest he fall again more swiftly than he hath risen, for by the blood of Christ I swear Liskyan will better adorn the purple shoes. Come, king of wrestlers! Whom the Tsar loves hath no need to fear a beggar. Array thy feet in majesty!"

Then the wrestler donned the purple shoes of the Tsar, and all who were gathered there acclaimed him, crying, "Hail, wearer of the purple!" And the wine flowed like a rosy river among them, and their clamor reached the very gates of heaven, offending the Lord. And louder than the cries of his fellows rang Basil's cries, but the wine from his beaker he spilled upon the ground.

And now the tapers burned low on a sorry sight, for many were fallen in the foulness they had made, and many clung in lust together, and Mihailo lay spread upon his couch in drunken slumber.

And Basil summoned the guard and said unto them: "Let the Tsar be borne to his chamber, and he who hath been honored by the Tsar laid at the foot of his bed." And so it was done.

And when all the palace slept, save only those who kept watch before their monarch's portal, Basil and his kinsmen crept with drawn swords upon them, and slaughtered them ere they might cry the alarm. And entering in, they slew Liskyan where he lay at the foot of the couch, and lifting high his sword, Basil severed

7

the hands of Mihailo from his arms, crying aloud: "Awake, my Lord, and receive thy scullion's homage."

And he awoke in anguish, making bitter moan, and he cried: "What hast thou done with me?"

And raising aloft the bleeding hands, his enemy cried: "Thy purple hands for the purple shoes of Liskyan, O Basileus, and my sword in thy heart for the words thou gavest me."

And he plunged his sword into Mihailo's heart, who groaned and perished, and in that chamber of blood the kinsmen of Basil knelt down before him, crying: "All hail, Tsar of the Greeks!"

Thus did the son of peasants gain Cæsar's throne, and the issue he begot in a harlot's womb ruled over the Greeks. But our people grew in grace and godliness, and as a mark of his favor, the Lord, from Whom all lovingkindness flows, bade those saintly men, Kyril the Wise and his brother Mefodius, write down in the tongue of our fathers His Blessèd Word, that its beauty might be revealed unto the eyes and ears of all his children. And many said: "This is a sin on your heads, for neither God nor the angels speak in the Serbian tongue, nor was it heard in the streets of Jerusalem, where Christ our Saviour walked of old."

But Kyril answered: "All things are from God, Whose name shall be praised in a multitude of tongues!" Nor did he cease from his labors till he had brought them to an end.

And he gave us the Holy Book, may his soul abide in everlasting light, and the wonders wrought by our Almighty Father, and the wisdom of His prophets and His saints. And those who had been loath to cast out the false gods from their hearts now spat upon them, and throughout all the land no Serb withheld his homage from the Lord Jehovah and His Only-Begotten Son.

So for long years we throve and multiplied, till the curse of Cain descended upon us, parting brother and brother. For ye must know that the Bulgars, having seized vast realms in the east, were grown to such might that Tsarigrad trembled before them and paid them tribute and bestowed upon their prince the crown of a Tsar. Yet there dwelt no peace between them, but each sought to wrest from the other what he had won.

And we had neither King nor Tsar to command us, but many zhupans, who strove against one another, for those there were who favored the cause of the Greeks, and those who fought with the Bulgar hordes. And this was a boon to the foe, destroying our strength that we might not stand against them, and they fell upon us, yea, Byzantine and Bulgar, and our name that had been a tower in the land crumbled to dust.

And at length it came to pass that another Basil, of the blood of Mihailo's slayer, mounted his throne, and he swore a mighty oath of vengeance against those who had humbled the head of Tsarigrad. And in that day Samuel ruled over the Bulgar tribes, having put to death his brothers and all their kin, save only Vladislav, son to his brother Aaron. For when the soldiers seized him to bear him away, the young Gavrilo, Samuel's son, sped to the Tsar, his father, crying: "My lord, thy soldiers have taken Vladislav, my comrade, to do him hurt. Bid them release him again, I pray thee, for I love him well and he hath done no wrong." And for Gavrilo's asking, the life of Vladislav was spared unto him.

And like two strong wrestlers, Basil and Samuel strove together, and now the palm was his and now his foe's, but neither might vanquish the other utterly.

OW there dwelt in Drach a Prince who was called Vladimir and was loved of the Lord, for he coveted not the kingdom of his neighbor, seeking only to rule in peace over the land that his fathers had bequeathed unto him. Wherefore he paid tribute to Tsarigrad and Basil named him friend.

But he that was Basil's friend was Samuel's foe, and the Bulgar lord arrayed his hosts against Vladimir and led them across the river to besiege the white city of Krayin. And the Prince, having been forewarned of his coming and being loath to shed his people's blood, took refuge with them in the fastnesses of the mountain Oblik, whither none might pursue him. And there the Almighty guarded His belovèd servant, for when the fire-snakes that flourish in the mountain Oblik crept forth from beneath the rocks, bruising the heel of man and beast that they perished, Vladimir cried: "Is it well done, O God, thus to afflict us? Hast Thou not said unto Thy children, 'Ye shall not kill,' and wilt Thou destroy us now with fire-snakes who have kept Thy law, and fled into these mountains lest our hands be steeped in the blood of our brothers?"

11

And God, seeing that the words of Vladimir were just, drew their venom from the tongues of the fire-snakes, that they struck in vain; yea, and even unto this day, he who will may wander unafraid in the mountain Oblik for the sake of the sign God showed to the blessèd Vladimir.

Yet man is inclined to evil as the Lord to good, and even as Judas of old betrayed his Master for thirty pieces of silver, so did the Zhupan Cvetko descend by night to the tent of Samuel and say unto him: "If thou wilt pay me richly, I will deliver Vladimir into thy hands."

And Samuel answered: "Nine tovars of gold will I pay thee, and thou shalt rule over a fair province, and be named Zhupan no longer, but Prince."

And Cvetko answered: "It is enough. Give me a band of forty, and they shall take Vladimir captive." And Samuel gave him a band of forty, whom he led through the darkness by hidden caverns and under swollen streams to Vladimir's refuge, where he slept among his nobles. And the Bulgar chieftain laid his foot on Vladimir's neck, crying: "Awake, thou Serb!"

And he awoke, and his warriors leaped to their feet, and seeing their lord surrounded, would have sped to his succor, but he cried: "Stand back, my children, and sheathe your swords again! Shall the flock defend the shepherd? Behold! Gladly do I yield myself up to these wolves! Let them devour me, but imperil not your souls for my worthless body. Vladimir, your Prince, commands it!"

And the Bulgar chieftain made mock of him, cry-

12

ing: "Yea, do thou come peacefully, thou faithful shepherd, and thy sheep shall return unmolested to their fold." And they bound his hands behind him and brought him before Samuel.

And Samuel questioned him, saying: "Wilt thou fight beside me, Vladimir, against the Greek? Then shall thy land and people be restored unto thee, and of all that we take from Basil half shall be thine."

But Vladimir answered: "I will not fight beside thee against any man. And if God will that thou rob me of what is mine, let His will be done, but for me, I may not put forth my hand to take what He hath destined for another."

"And will God break for thee the bars of my dungeon, thou simple fool, where the flesh shall rot from thy bones, and vermin corrupt thee while thou art yet in life?"

"Thou hast no bars so thick that He may not shatter them, nor any dungeon so deep that He may not enter in. Yet, though He give thee power over my flesh, still will I praise Him, for wert thou fifty times the Bulgar Tsar thou canst not harm my soul, that is in His keeping."

Then Samuel commanded that Vladimir be brought in chains to Presba, but himself, seeking vengeance, went like a burning wind through all Pomorye, and, where he set his foot, the land that had bloomed in plenty withered and perished. And when he had had his fill of vengeance, he returned to Presba and sought out Vladimir, who languished in his deepest dungeon, and said unto him: "Thy country is laid waste, and thy

13

cities are burned to the ground, and the remnant of thy people that my sword hath spared are fled into the mountains, and among the ruins thy mother weeps for her son. But if thou wilt fight beside me against the Greek, I will sow thy land anew with fields and vineyards and build up thy cities and call thy people from the mountains where they hunger and thirst, and restore thee to the heart of thy mother. And thou shalt be second to none save Samuel. Will God do more?"

And Vladimir cried: "He will keep me in the hollow of His hand, He will shelter me beneath the shadow of His pinions, He will fold me within His breast, and I shall dwell in the light of His love forever."

"Thou shalt dwell forever in the darkness of this charnel-house, and worms shall eat thee." And having spoken, Samuel departed in wrath to his high tower, but the soul of Vladimir was at peace.

And when the season of the Lord's agony drew nigh, Kossara, daughter to Samuel, whom he loved, said unto him: "I would go with my maidens into the dungeons, my father, and wash the feet of thy captives, that God, leaning down from His throne, may see how we humble ourselves on this dread day before His vilest creatures."

And he answered: "Do as thy heart bids thee, my daughter."

So she went down with her maidens to the dungeons, and with clear water they cleansed, and with fair kerchiefs dried the feet of the captives, and came in the end to that foul cell where Vladimir ceased not from

14

prayer. And Kossara, looking upon him, was filled with wonder, for his beauty was as the beauty of the morning star, shining at dawn over the fair land of Illyria.

And she said: "Whence art thou, and wherefore doth my father hold thee captive?"

And he answered: "I am Vladimir, Prince in Serbia and ruler over Drach, and thy father holds me captive, because I will not fight beside him against the Greek."

Then she cried: "O thou bright Prince, do thou make peace with him, and thou shalt be my bridegroom, for in truth I love thee. No mother hath borne a fairer son than thine."

"Happy is he who wins thee for his bride, lovely Kossara, yet I may not do thy father's will. Since Cain slew Abel, the Lord hath said: 'Thou shalt not shed the blood of thy brother!' Then shall I deny my God, whether it be for the favor of a tsar or a fair maid's hand?"

And Kossara fell silent, standing before him like a scarlet-footed bird whose song is stilled in her throat, and at length she left him. But his memory burned in her breast, and on the morrow she came again to his cell, crying: "Teach me how thou dost serve the Lord, Vladimir, that I may serve Him likewise." And leaning his golden head between the bars, he taught her the way of godliness, and his words were sweeter to her than sweet honey.

So day by day she drank wisdom at his lips, till Gavrilo her brother chided her, saying: "What kindness moves thee toward this captive, sister? Dost thou

15

labor for his soul? Then our father's dungeons are filled with groaning men in need of solace, though they be neither young nor comely nor golden-haired. Now I charge thee, go not again to Vladimir but abide among thy maidens, lest the Tsar, learning of these things, be angered against thee."

And she cried: "Dost thou think to affright me, my brother? Truly I love this captive, neither for the sake of his youth nor his comeliness nor his golden hair, but because he speaks with God. And I will go to my father and unbind my tresses and bow down before him, kissing his hands and knees, and I will rain my tears upon his feet, but I will not leave him till he hath pledged me in marriage to Vladimir. For though he slay me, I will wed no other."

And she went to the gray tower of Samuel, and unbound her tresses and bowed down before him, kissing his hands and knees, and she rained her tears upon his feet, and he cried: "What is thy grief, my daughter? Wherefore dost thou kneel before me, thy garments awry and thy black hair unbound, uttering lamentation? What boon dost thou seek, my fawn, that thy sire will not grant thee?"

"My father, my lord, I know that thou wilt give me one day in marriage to some alien prince, yet now I say to thee, I love Vladimir whom thou dost hold in bondage, and though thou slay me I will wed no other."

"Vladimir is thy father's foe."

"Nay, he is no man's foe, but all men are his

16

brothers, and he will not draw his sword against them."

Then the heart of Samuel, who had slain his brother Aaron, was wrung as by the hand of God, and his bones melted within him and his marrow withered, and all he had wrought was as a mound of dust upon his tongue. And he raised his daughter from the earth, saying: "Dry thy tears and bind up thy tresses again, and wed whom thou wilt," and he gave her the key that unsealed the dungeon of Vladimir, saying: "Release thy bridegroom."

Thus was Kossara's grief turned to rejoicing, and she laid her white cheek in love on her father's hand, then sped below, light as the summer wind that treads upon the flowers, yet bows them not beneath her tread. And she cried: "I come, Vladimir. It is Kossara, thy bride, who brings thee freedom and the golden sun and an end to weeping." And she unsealed his dungeon, and from his arms and legs and his white throat the gaoler struck his cruel fetters, and the maiden led him forth into the light.

And he fell upon his knees, crying: "Praise be to God, and to thee, Kossara, who art His handmaid," and she knelt beside him, offering thanksgiving to the Lord. Then, laying her white hand in his, she brought him to the tower of Samuel.

And Samuel cried: "Thou hast vanquished me, Vladimir."

And he answered: "Not I, O Tsar, but the Lord hath vanquished thee, which is glory and no shame."

"It may be as thou hast said. Yet I have unbound

thee by my daughter's will, because her desire is for thee, and because thou art a prince, young and well-favored and worthy to be her bridegroom. Say, wilt thou take her for thy bride, Vladimir?"

"As I would take fire to warm me, and water to slake my thirst and bread to solace me." ·

Then Samuel commanded that his son be bathed and anointed with sweet-smelling oils and arrayed in scarlet, and the wedding feast was spread, and Kossara went forth in beauty to meet her lord. And they took their way to the church of the holy Achilleios of Larissa, he whose bones Samuel had borne in triumph out of Thessaly, and the Patriarch laid their hands like two fair doves upon one another, binding them with the sacred kerchief, and joined in wedlock Vladimir the Prince to Kossara, daughter of the mighty Bulgar Tsar.

And returning to the castle, they were welcomed with song and merrymaking, and minstrels played upon the flute and tambour, and maidens danced the kolo, and where hatred and black wrath had been were love and gladness.

And for seven days they feasted, and when the feasting was at an end, Samuel said: "Return in peace to Drach, my children. And my builders shall build up your walls and towers, fairer than before, and my plowmen shall sow your fields with plenty. And do thou, Kossara, bear heroes unto thy lord and daughters comely as their mother. And do thou, Vladimir, cherish her kindly who hath given thee life for death." And he blessed them and kissed them upon either cheek and bade them farewell.

So they journeyed to Drach, and when the people learned that their well-loved lord had been restored unto them, they came down into the valleys, praising the name of the All-Merciful, and went forth with trumpets and cymbals to welcome him, and brought him again to the throne of his fathers. And the mother of Vladimir led the daughter of Samuel to her place beside her lord, and all the court bowed down in homage before them.

And they ruled justly, walking in the fear of God, and their souls were as clear pools that held the sky. And so measureless was their love for one another that it overflowed their hearts, watering the land, that blossomed like the garden of Paradise. But no serpent dwelt therein, and each man was the friend of his brother, and the golden sun shone over all.

19

ponless to battle? Look forth! Am I grown so weak that mine enemy comes with naked hands against me? The sun shines down upon them, yet shines on neither shield nor saber. Now mount thy steed, and ride boldly to meet this army, and when thou hast learned to what end they march upon us, as boldly return."

And having spoken, Samuel looked again from the casement, and his boyars gathered about him, and Gavrilo, his son, stood at his right hand, yet he heeded them not, but still his enchanted gaze clung to that dark stream that welled without end above the crest of the mountain and down its slope. And he beat his breast, groaning aloud in his anguish, yet knew not that he groaned nor beat his breast.

And his messenger, riding as for the sake of God, now galloped into sight, now vanished behind a wall of stone, and was drawn at length into the shadow of those he had gone to meet as into the maw of some creeping monster, that held him for a space, then spat him forth again to the white road. And back he sped so swiftly that the eye might not follow his course, and crossed the moat, and mounted into the tower, and flung himself at the feet of Samuel. And his body shook and his eyes were the eyes of one who hath looked on doom, and though he strove to speak, no word issued from his mouth but only sounds of madness.

Then Samuel thrust him away, and looking neither to the right nor left, strode from the tower, whence none dared follow, and those who beheld his face fled from before him. Only the agèd monk Ilarion

22

went by his side, knowing no fear of his master, since all his fear and all his hope rested in the Lord. And when the Tsar rode forth from the gate to meet what God had sent, the holy man toiled after him.

And midway of the mountain, there where the white road turns between two crags that stretch toward heaven, Samuel checked his steed, as a line of moving men appeared to his sight, and the hand of each man clasped his comrade's shoulder, for his eyes were blinded, and only to him who led them had the light of a single eye been spared.

And by that light he saw the face of his sovereign, and fell prone before him, crying: "Hail to thee, Tsar, in the name of Basil the Greek, who bids me speak for him in this wise: 'Out of my mercy I have sent back to thee thy fifteen thousand Bulgars taken captive in Makedon. And I have blinded them, leaving an eye to one in every hundred, that he might lead his brothers home. They will fight for thee no more, O Samuel, but let them be thy guslars, to go up and down in the land, rejoicing thy people with the tale of thy wondrous deeds.' "

And as lightning smites the lord of the forest that, groaning, he sways, and swaying, crashes to earth, so did the words of his enemy smite Samuel from his steed, stretching him by the roadside. And his mantle covered his face, and his faithful charger stood guard above him. But those whom Basil had blinded went on their way, the hand of each man clasping his comrade's shoulder.

And when the monk Ilarion found the Tsar, he drew

23

away the mantle that hid his face, and knelt down beside him, and chanted above him the prayers that are prayed for the dead.

And Samuel being laid to rest with his fathers, Gavrilo ruled on his throne. But his rule was troubled, for the sire's might abode not in the son, and Vladislav, whom he had saved from a cruel death, looked now with alien eyes upon him, and sowed mischief among his people, saying: "Because ye named him Tsar, on whose brow lay the mark of Cain, God chastens you. Nor will He forsake His wrath till the usurper be hurled from his place, and your destined monarch anointed."

And Basil the Greek, learning of these things, took counsel with his crafty heart, and sent his messenger unto Vladislav, saying: "How long wilt thou hold thy hand? Whom dost thou fear, Samuel being dead? Brothers are we in hatred of him and all his line, wherefore, when thou hast slain Gavrilo and taken his kingdom, like a brother will I sustain thee, and he who offends thee shall answer unto Tsarigrad."

Now the words of Basil were to Vladislav as the goad to a willing steed, and as Gavrilo hunted in the forest, he came behind him and drew his sword and slew him, crying: "Thy death for my father's and thy crown for me!"

And none dared oppose him, for his strength was

great in the land because of Aaron his father, and the priests anointed him, and the boyars bowed down before him and the people acclaimed him Tsar. And he commanded that the wife and babes of Gavrilo be put to the sword, together with all who had held him dear, and so it was done.

Then Vladislav bethought him of Vladimir, Kossara's lord, who ruled in Drach, and sent his messenger with gentle words to the Prince, saying: "Are we not kinsmen and shall we not bestow upon each other the kiss of friendship? With honor would I welcome thee to Presba where once thou didst drag thy chainèd feet. Wherefore tarry not, but come, together with Kossara thy wife, and accept in token of my faith the gift I send thee."

And the messenger laid into the hand of Vladimir a cross of gold, richly wrought and encrusted with glowing jewels, and he would have raised it to his lips but Kossara rose from her place beside him, crying: "Go not, my lord, I pray thee. The gift is false as the heart of him who gave it, and will betray thee. Go not, my husband, nor put thy faith in this breaker of oaths, lest it be with thee as with Gavrilo whom he slew."

Then Vladimir spoke to the messenger and said: "Restore his gift to thy master and say to him that neither on gold nor silver was our Saviour martyred, but on a cross of wood. Then if his truth be truth indeed, let him send me by the hand of his bishop a cross of the cypress-tree, and gladly will I go to receive and bestow upon him the kiss of friendship."

25

And the messenger bore his words to Vladislav who rejoiced to hear them, and he summoned the Archbishop David and said unto him: "Vladimir hath disdained my gift, saying: 'Neither on gold nor silver was our Saviour martyred, but on a cross of cypress wood.' Go therefore, and be my messenger, and take this cross of cypress to the Prince to be a sign of faith between us, for my soul is weary of slaughter and cries out for peace."

And David answered: "Blessèd be the All-Righteous, who hath given thee another heart," and went forth on his way.

But Kossara, fearing still for her lord, knew no peace either by day or night, and at length she said unto him: "I would make a pilgrimage, my husband, to Elbassan and pray the saintly Yovan to shield us from peril. And I will light a taper high as heaven to shine before his eyes, that he cannot choose but look down upon me and heed my prayer."

And smiling upon her, Vladimir answered: "What dost thou fear, my dove, since there is no death without the appointed day, and if God wills it, all the saints together may not help. Yet make thy pilgrimage, if it pleases thee, and light thy taper, and pray to the saintly Yovan to give thee peace."

Now David the Archbishop, far on his way to Drach, encountered a company of horsemen in whose midst a litter was borne, and he said: "God be your guide and lead you to your journey's end. Whom do ye bear in the litter?"

"The Lady Kossara, daughter to Samuel, and wife of Vladimir our Prince."

"Then are we well met. Say to the Lady Kossara that I come from Vladislav, and journey to her lord, bearing a cross of cypress wood to be a pledge of faith between them."

And hearing these tidings, Kossara went forth to greet the holy man. And she said: "Shrive me, my father, for I have sinned, beguiling my well-loved lord. 'I will go to Elbassan,' I said, 'and pray for peace.' Yet my way lies not toward Elbassan but Presba, and I would pray not to the saintly Yovan, but to the God-forsaken Vladislav, in whose honeyed words I put no trust. For why should he that slew my brother and his wife and harmless babes seek friendship now with us?"

And he answered: "For thy sin, it is pardoned thee. For thy fear, banish it altogether from thy breast. By the hand of the church doth the Tsar send his peace-offering, a cross of that sacred wood whereon our Lord endured his agony. Truly, he hath been bathed in blood-guilt, yet he dare not take the name of Christ in vain and flout God himself. Nay, be of good cheer, my daughter, and go thy way, and when thou art come to Presba, say to the Tsar that Vladimir follows thee." And weeping, she clung to his knees and cried:

27

"Thrice blest art thou, whose path leads thee to my lord. Greet him, I pray thee, in Kossara's name, and say that though I have deceived him, yet I love him more than my life, and in Presba I will await his coming."

And David blessed her and bade her farewell and followed the road to Drach. But Kossara went on her way to Presba, and ere she had reached the castle gate, the horsemen of the Tsar rode forth to do her honor, and his trumpeters hailed her, and within the court his boyars greeted her and led her into his presence.

And he said: "Thou art welcome, Kossara, and would I might have welcomed thy husband beside thee."

And she answered: "Without his knowledge am I come before him, to plead with thee. I fear thee, Vladislav. Thy words are gentle, but thy hands reek with the blood of all my father's house. Now if thou be still hot for vengeance on his children yet unborn, slay me, his daughter, for they will grow in my womb, and my blood will feed them, and they will drink hatred of thee at my white breasts. But for my husband, what hath he to do with Samuel and thy wrongs?"

"Neither he nor thou, Kossara, for my wrongs are righted. These woes are not of my making, but were born on that ancient day when Samuel plunged his sword into my father's heart, robbing me of my birthright. Now that which was done is undone, and my soul, weary of slaughter, cries out to thee for peace.

28

Let us bury hatred, for by that sacred cross now lying on Vladimir's breast, I swear there is no guile in me."

And she answered: "Let be what will be. I can do no more."

But hidden behind dense thickets that bordered the highway where, seeing, they were yet unseen, the archers of the Tsar awaited Vladimir's coming, to slay him by their master's command. Yet the Lord, loath that His saint should perish in that secret place, sent His angels to go before him, and those in ambush, hearing the sound of hoofbeats and thinking to behold a mortal prince, beheld a wingèd host, arrayed in glory, and bearing swords of flame. And powerless to stay their hands, they let fly their arrows, but the flaming swords turned them aside from their mark, and sped them back, each to the heart of its sender.

And Vladimir went unharmed on his way by David's side, and when they were come to the church of the holy Achilleios, he said: "I will go in and praise the Lord, Who hath brought me to my journey's end."

Now David's messenger sought audience of the Tsar as he feasted in his golden hall, and kneeling before him, cried: "God save thee, sire! Vladimir the Serb hath entered within thy gates and prays to the Lord in the church of Achilleios."

Then the Tsar leaped from his place, crying: "Let that prayer be his last! Surround the church, ye Bulgars, and slay him by whatsoever means ye may, for if he escape you a second time, ye shall pay with your heads."

And they hastened forth and surrounded the church of Achilleios, and Vladimir, ceasing from prayer, beheld through the casement their lances and their keen-edged swords.

And he spoke to the Archbishop David, saying: "What hast thou done, my lord? Wherefore hast thou betrayed me who trusted in thee?" And David, seeing what the Tsar had wrought, might answer no word, but for shame and sorrow his head hung low on his breast.

Then Vladimir kissed the cross sent by his foe as a pledge of faith between them, and bade farewell to those who had borne him company from Drach, and laid his hand in blessing on David's head, saying: "Weep not, my father, but pray unto the Lord to receive my soul." And raising the cross on high, he went forth from the church, and the Bulgars seized him and smote his head from his shoulders.

But when they would have borne his body to the Tsar, David suffered them not, saying: "Ye have done your task. Now let him rest in God."

And Vladimir lay that night within the church where once he had been wedded to Kossara, and tapers burned at his head, and his white hands that were folded upon his breast held the cross of his betrayal.

And suddenly the tapers burning at his head were quenched, though no hand had profaned them, and

there where his neck had received the sword-stroke
shone a wondrous light that grew and spread, filling all
the church with its radiance, and his martyred limbs
gave forth the fragrance of myrrh and balsam, and
from on high the voices of a heavenly host chanted
glory to the Lord.

And those who kept vigil fell prostrate before him,
heavy with dread of the sin that defiled their land, and
Vladislav trembled to hear this omen of the wrath to
come. And thinking to avert God's vengeance, he suffered Kossara to bear her husband's body to Krayin
where, amid bitter tears, she laid him to rest in the
church he had built to the Blessèd Mother of Christ.
And many came to worship at his shrine, and to all
who were pure in heart God answered the prayers they
prayed at the tomb of Vladimir.

And Kossara dwelt as a nun within the cloister, but
her years were few, for the Lord took compassion upon
her, releasing from bondage her weary soul that
soared, exulting, to heaven. But her body reposed at
the feet of her dear-loved Prince.

And in after days they were laid amid the cypress-
trees of Elbassan, and each year at Whitsuntide ere
the coming of dawn, Vladimir's cross is borne by pious
hands from its resting-place to the top of the mountain
Rumiya, and so bright is the splendor of his name that
pilgrims from far and near, yea, heathen and right-
believers, clasp hands to follow in its wake. And they
reach the mountain's height with the rising sun, and
there they pour forth their hearts in song to the Giver

31

of all Good, and pray for the peace of His gracious Saint Vladimir.

But the wicked Vladislav, who had thought to reap joy of his wickedness, reaped death and woe. For even as he had broken faith with the Serb, so did the Greek break faith with him, making mock of his pledge, and assailing him on every hand.

And it came to pass that they strove together for the white city of Krayin, and Basil took her stronghold, and the tents of the Bulgars lay beneath her walls. And on the eve of battle Vladislav feasted in his tent, raising his chalice to drink to the morrow's hap. But suddenly his fingers loosed their hold, letting fall the cup that stained his garments with wine redder than blood, and he cried: "Shield me, my children! Vladimir comes to take my life!"

And where his eyes were fixed in anguish, theirs followed and beheld an angel standing, whose countenance was the countenance of Vladimir, and whose naked sword was turned on their master's breast. And they sat as though death had stricken them, moving neither hand nor foot, but Vladislav, like one who goes in a dream, went forth from his place and fell upon the edge of the angel's sword and perished.

RAISE be to God, Who orders all things in the light of His wisdom, and metes out justice soon or late! Now the Bulgars, having trampled the Serbs underfoot, were themselves laid low, and Basil triumphed, making himself lord over all Illyria. Glorious in conquest, he entered the Golden Gate of Tsarigrad, and the people crowned him with garlands, crying: "Hail, Bulgar-slayer! Hail, master of the world! Hail, king of kings!" And maidens went before him, strewing blossoms, and the wife of Vladislav went in chains behind. And at the portal of Saint Sofia the Patriarch welcomed him, blessing him in the name of the All-High, and led him into the church where great and lowly lifted their voices in glad hallelujahs to Him Who had turned the splendor of His countenance upon them.

And while Basil reigned, and for many generations thereafter, the princes and zhupans of the Serbian land paid tribute to the Greek, and sent him as hostages their sons and kinsmen, and were subject to his will. And though they strove ever and again to throw off his yoke, they strove in vain till it pleased the Lord to call the mighty Nemanya to their aid. For whereas he had set tsars to rule the Greeks, and kings to hold sway over the Magyar tribes, out of his boundless mercy and because he was loath that they should be destroyed, he gave unto the Serbs a Grand Zhupan, on whom was bestowed in holy baptism the name of Stefan Nemanya.

Son to Zavida the Prince, he who was destined to lead his people from chains to golden freedom throve in the house of his father, surpassing all men in stature and the wisdom of his heart. Wherefore God gave him power over them, and though he was the last-born among his brothers, the people named him Grand Zhupan.

And he called together the chieftains and the lesser zhupans, and said unto them: "Why are ye out of favor with Heaven? Because strife and hatred flourish among you, and each man covets the treasure of his neighbor. Because thieves are your judges and evil-doers sit in your high places. Because your swords, that should be keen for your foe, are blunted with your brothers' blood. Now therefore do I ordain that he who robs his neighbor shall be robbed of the sight of his eyes; and he who bears false witness, his tongue

34

shall be plucked forth at the root, and he who makes war on his brother shall be put to death."

And because his words were just and his arm was strong, Nemanya bent them to his will, bringing order out of confusion, and out of weakness strength. And all the Serbian lands fell under his dominion, and he made peace with Venice and with the Magyar tribes. And he took to his wife the Serbian Princess Ana, who bore him Vukan and Stefan.

But still he paid tribute to Tsarigrad, where Manuel ruled, biding the time when he might rise up against him. And lest the Greek should doubt him, he journeyed to his golden city and appeared, barefoot and bare of head, before his throne. And a rope lay about his neck and, falling prone at the feet of Manuel, he proffered his sword in sign of his fealty. And those who beheld him marveled, for it was as though a mountain lay at the foot of a hill.

O, PRESENTLY, he returned to Rashka, and being hot with love for the blessèd Lord Jesus, vowed that he would build Him a church at the mouth of the river Banska and a dwelling-house for the holy brethren, where they might worship Him from dawn to dark, and pray for the soul of the mighty Nemanya and for all his seed. And he journeyed with the Lady Ana and his builders and servants into the wild country of Toplitsa, and from the face of the mountain was the rock hewn and the church reared to the memory of the good Saint Nikola, and a dwelling-house for the holy brethren, and a towered wall to fold them within its shelter.

But ere the last stone had been laid, it chanced one day that Nemanya walked alone in a green valley, and came on a shepherd maid among her sheep who raised her black eyes to his, yet spoke no word and went her way. And her glance was as a draught of strong wine unto the Grand Zhupan, and his limbs trembled and through his veins the blood raged like Morava's torrent, so fierce was his desire for the maid. And returning to his people, he bade them seek her out and bring her to him when the moon was dark, that he might lie with her.

Now the holy brethren learned of Nemanya's purpose and were sore distressed, for they feared lest the deed dishonor the doer and shame the memory of the good Saint Nikola whom they would have exalted. Wherefore they sent one of their number to the Lady Ana, who was wise as she was fair, and he told her of the Grand Zhupan's encounter in the valley with the shepherd maid and of the command he had laid upon his people.

And having heard the tale to its close, she smiled and said: "Let not the maid come nigh unto my lord, and I will turn aside his wrath, that it smite neither the servants who have served him ill, nor you who have betrayed him into my hands."

And so it was done. And when the moon was dark, one who went garbed in the dress of a shepherd maid stole into Nemanya's tent and let fall her garments, and her beauty gleamed in the shadows like the beauty of a silver birch amid pine-trees. And rejoicing, he bore her to his couch, where her white arms held him as a blossom holds in sweetness the questing bee who, having drunk his fill, sinks into slumber within the chalice that hath nourished him.

And presently she waked him, saying: "Suffer me to leave thee, my lord, that I may return to my sheep under the eyes of the stars who will not chide me."

And he answered: "Go in peace, thou who hast brought me joy, but take with thee some mark of my favor, that men may know thou hast pleased a prince."

And she said: "I will take the jewel from thy finger, if thou wilt give it me."

And he gave her the jewel from his finger, and she went from him into the darkness of night and he saw her no more. For with the first dawn came a messenger to Nemanya from Manuel the Tsar, bidding him lead his hosts against the heathen, Arslan. And straightway he sent the Lady Ana, guarded by a stout company, to Ras his stronghold, but himself he rode to the south, where for many moons he battled with his foe, ere he routed them and drove them into the desert and set his face again toward Ras. And as he passed through the gates of his walled city, the people welcomed him, crying: "Hail, Serbian hero! Hail, thou bane of the infidel!" And in the court his steward knelt before him, crying: "Hail, father of three sons!"

And Nemanya laughed that the tears ran into his beard and he cried: "Hath joy so addled thee that thou canst no longer count thy master's sons? Vukan have I begot, my eldest-born, and Stefan, the second, but who the third may be I know not, O keeper of my household!"

And the steward answered: "He lies new-born in the chamber of thy wife."

Then Nemanya leaped from his steed and his eyes burned like the eyes of a wolf in the thicket that crouches ere he springs upon his prey. And swiftly he went to the chamber of the Lady Ana and found her with the babe on her white breast, and drawing his sword, he cried: "Now die, thou harlot, together with

38

the bastard thou hast borne," but when he would have fallen upon her, his hand was stayed as by some unseen power. And he saw that her eyes held neither shame nor fear but only gladness.

And she spoke softly, saying: "Smite, if it be thy will, my lord, yet thou wilt slay neither harlot nor bastard, but thy faithful wife and the true-born child of thy loins."

Then harshly he bade her say how this thing might be, and she drew from her finger the jewel he had worn in the mountains of Toplitsa and gave it into his hand, saying: "By this mark of thy favor shall it be known to men that Ana hath pleased a prince."

And the Grand Zhupan would have bowed his head in repentance before his wife that he had accused her, but she suffered him not, saying: "Do thou grant me thy pardon, my husband, that I took from thee by guile what thou gavest not."

And he answered: "Let us seek and grant forgiveness, each of the other, and for the child, let him be called Rastko, that he may grow in glory beyond his sire."

And the child was sprayed with holy water, and named with the name of Rastko, and he grew in strength and beauty, excelling his brothers in the arts of the sword and the chase, yet loving learning and reading each day in the sacred books of the church, till his face was filled with light and his heart with wisdom. And he was beloved of all men, but to his parents dearer than their dearest treasure.

N THE fullness of his years, Manuel the Tsar was gathered unto his fathers, and his land was delivered over to warring lords who, for the terror that raged within their borders, heeded not the peril without.

And Nemanya, seeing the hand of God herein, struck swiftly, laying waste many fair cities from Sritsa to Prizren. And the mighty walls of Nish he razed to earth, and white Skoplie, leaving no stone on stone to bear witness to their ancient pride, but only a desolation and a wilderness for the crying of winds.

And he seized high Zeta, and with sword and arrow scattered the Greeks who dwelt against God's will on those pleasant slopes. And their gold and treasure he meted out among his nobles, leaving two tithes for the church, and their vineyards he gave unto the planters of vines and their cattle unto the herdsmen. So his people abode again in the land of their fathers, but Nemanya with all his court tarried in Ras.

May the kingdom of heaven and peace eternal be thine, O Serbia's sun, who through the grace of the Lord brought these things to pass!

40

Then Ysaak Angelos, having mounted the throne of the East, proffered his hand in friendship to the Grand Zhupan, and he said: "Let the lion consort with the lion, that their seed may mingle and rule over all the earth. And if thou art content, I will send thee the Princess Yevdokia to be wife to thy son Stefan." And Nemanya was content.

Now when Rastko had completed eighteen years, Nemanya, his father, sought for him a bride, and sent messengers throughout his kingdom to make choice of the fairest. And many were brought before him but pleased him not, till at length he beheld the maiden Churchinka, black-browed and red and white, a slender ivory tower bathed in sunlight. And he said: "Thou shalt be the bride of Rastko."

And he summoned Rastko to his presence, addressing him with joyful words: "Make ready, my son, for thou shalt be wed to the maiden Churchinka."

But Rastko answered: "I would not grieve thee, my father, nor offend thee in aught, yet my heart is wedded to holiness, and I may not take an earthly bride."

And Nemanya waxed wroth with him, crying: "If thou be wedded in truth to holiness, then heed the Lord's command that bids thee bow to the will of thy sire, nor depart from the path he hath marked out for thee."

And the youth answered: "In all things save in this will I do thy bidding, but as the heavens are high above the earth, so is the will of my heavenly Father exalted above thine."

Then did the fires of Nemanya's spirit leap in fierce rage, and he lifted his arm and would have destroyed his son, who quailed not before him, but again, as at the touch of some unseen power, it fell harmless by his side. And he said: "Praised be the Lord, Who hath saved me from the sin of thy death, yet I call Him to witness that the maid I have chosen for thee thou shalt surely wed."

And he sealed Rastko within his chamber, denying him both food and drink, save for a crust and a cup of clear water that the servant laid before him at sundown. But Rastko ate not of the crust, nor drank of the water, neither on the first day, nor on the second or third, till at length the Lady Ana besought her lord with tears, crying: "When thou wouldst have slain our son by the sword, God suffered thee not. Wilt thou slay him now by hunger and by thirst?"

And the Prince answered: "He shall do my will."

"Then send to him the maiden Churchinka, that by her arts she may move him to do thy will."

And they sent the maiden Churchinka to his chamber, and she stood before him, black-browed and red and white, a slender ivory tower bathed in sunlight. Yet he looked not upon her, but only on the words of the Holy Book outspread to his eyes.

42

And she spake to him softly, saying: "Wilt thou not look upon me, Rastko, for I am fair, and the heart is wiser than the book."

But he answered: "And wert thou fair as the mountain Veela, and wiser than the serpent of Paradise, I desire thee not. For I am wedded to holiness, and I will perish, but I will not lie in sin with an earthly maid."

"Then lie with me not, but wed me to please thy sire, and when we are brought to bed, I will veil myself from thy sight, and sleep beside thee as a sister beside her brother."

But he answered naught, nor raised his glance from the blessèd words of the Book. And drawing nigh, she laid her white hand on his and whispered: "Dost thou fear me, Rastko, that thou wilt not look upon me?"

Then he flung her from him, crying: "I fear thee not, nor thy works. For I know thee what thou art, thou lure of Satan and tempter of the flesh. Now get thee gone, for me thou shalt not lure, nor in any wise entice into thy snare, since the Lord of the righteous is my shield."

And as he spoke, a radiance brighter than the noonday sun clothed him as in a fiery garment, blinding the maid, and she fled from him in terror and cast herself at the feet of the Grand Zhupan. And she cried: "Thy son was not born to be husband to a maid, for when I would have laid my hand in boldness upon him, God blinded me." And weeping, she went her way.

But the heart of Nemanya was hardened against his son, and he heeded neither the words of Churchinka, nor his lady's tears. And it chanced that three monks of the Holy Mountain of Athos made pilgrimage to Ras to sue for alms, and came that day before the Grand Zhupan. And he said to them: "If ye will wrestle with my son, and lead him back to the way of duty, your camels shall be laden with treasure and your asses with more gold than they can bear."

So the monks were led to the chamber of Rastko and beheld him, a comely youth, with hair of gold and the golden garb of a prince, whose eyes were fixed on the words of the Holy Book, outspread before him.

And Arseni, the eldest among them, a good and ancient man, spoke to Rastko, saying: "Thou art fair, my child, and thy spirit is lit by God, for thou readest in the sacred Book. Then wherefore doth thy father make plaint against thee?"

And Rastko answered: "He would have me wed an earthly maid, but I may not, for the beauty of God's Word hath beguiled my spirit, and I crave no dearer bride."

Then they questioned him, wondering at the wisdom of one so young and the treasure of his learning. And at length Arseni said: "The Lord hath bidden man honor his father, truly, yet hath He not also

44

bidden him render unto God the things that are from God? And the wisdom of this youth is from God, and his piety, and his ardent spirit, and his love of righteousness. And meet it is that he should render them back in service to Him Who gave them. Wherefore, bright Prince, if thou speak soberly, and wilt put off thy royal raiment for the habit of a monk, then come with us to Athos, and we will guide thee on the good path thou hast chosen."

And Rastko answered: "Right willingly, holy father, yet how shall I escape from this sealed chamber and my sire's wrath?"

"By guile shalt thou escape, and God will forgive us the sin for the blessings that shall spring therefrom. For lo! we will gladden the heart of Nemanya, saying: 'Our prayers have moved thy son.' And when he hath laden our camels with treasure and our asses with gold, and we are departed on the way to Athos, do thou, my son, seek thy father's gracious leave to go forth at dawn with thy comrades and men-at-arms to hunt in the forest. Having gained its shelter, give spurs unto thy steed, and ride swiftly to the mouth of the Eunuch's Cavern, where we will await thee."

And as the good Arseni counseled, so did they. Joyfully did the Grand Zhupan receive their tidings, and in the gladness of his heart brought forth from his treasure-house all manner of rich gifts to be their guerdon. And when he had sped them on their way, he summoned Rastko, who knelt before his father and said: "Forgive me my ill deeds, and grant my prayer. My body is wasted with fasting and the shedding of many tears. Wherefore, I beseech thee, suffer me to go forth at dawn to the hunt, that the mountain winds may cleanse me and make me whole."

And Nemanya blessed him to go forth to the hunt, and the Lady Ana kissed his white brow, and at dawn, amid the baying of hounds and the crying of falcons and the sweet call of the horns, he left his father's castle, and rode with his comrades and his men-at-arms into the forest. And suddenly, giving spurs to his steed, he outstripped his fellows and reached the mouth of the Eunuch's Cavern, where the monks awaited him. Now the beasts they had driven into the cave, lest their cries betray them, but for themselves, they fled to the clefts in the mountainside, where no steed might pursue them, nor any hound discern their track.

And those who had borne Rastko company sought him till the coming of night, sounding their horns on the mountaintop, and calling on his name through all the valleys. But they sought in vain, and when darkness fell, and they could see neither the mountains nor valleys nor the ears of their steeds, they must needs return to Ras with their ill tidings.

And hearing them, Nemanya spoke no word, but his head drooped from his shoulders like the crest of a mighty oak, whose roots have been torn by gales out of the earth. And for three days he sat without food or drink, till the Lady Ana drew nigh and spake to him words of comfort and of healing: "Is thy grief greater than mine, my lord, that have sheltered the child within my womb, and borne him in pain and fed him with the milk of my white breasts? Wherefore dost thou mourn, as though death had laid him forever from thy sight? Rejoice rather that he is in life and health, and that the Lord will grant thee to look again on his face."

And Nemanya said: "He hath flouted me, and gone from the house of his father to the house of strangers."

"Who knows if he hath not been led by the hand of God? Hear me, my husband, and if my words lack reason, never heed me more. Send thy messengers to the Holy Mountain, whither Rastko is fled with the monks who visited thee. Let them question him. It may be that ere now he hath rued his flight. Yet if he be steadfast still and firm in his faith, is it so bitter to thee indeed, my lord, that our son should be called to do God's work among men?"

Then Nemanya arose from his place, and bathed his hands in clear water, and bade his servants bring him food and drink, and embraced his wife, and said: "The Lord hath laid His words upon thy tongue."

And he summoned his nobles, and chose from among their number a score of valiant warriors, and placing at their head his son Vukan, he charged them seek out his youngest-born on the Holy Mountain, and try if they might in any wise win him back to the life of the world. "Yet constrain him not, but if he come not freely, leave him in peace."

Now from the mountain clefts, when his comrades had ceased from calling and the sound of the blowing of horns could be heard no longer, Rastko and the holy fathers came forth, and driving before them

47

their beasts of burden, set out upon their journey in the darkness of night. And they knew no fear of man or evil spirit, or the raging torrent or the chasm that opened at their feet. For God went before them, and whom God guides what hand will lead astray?

And Rastko drew the golden shoes from his feet, and went unshod over stone and briar, till those who went with him cried out to see the red blood flowing from his tender flesh. But the Prince laughed, and sang, as he journeyed, the songs of David, King of the Israelites: "As the hart panteth after the water brooks, so panteth my soul after Thee, O God. My tears have been my meat day and night; gather Thou my tears into Thy vial. I am become a stranger unto my brethren and an alien unto my mother's children. Whom have I in heaven but Thee? And there is none upon earth that I desire beside Thee. Thou hast delivered my soul from death. Wilt Thou not deliver my feet from falling, O God?"

And his comrades joined their tongues to his in praise of the Lord, and so with prayer and singing they came at last to the Holy Mountain, and it was as though they had journeyed but an hour.

And they entered Saint Pantelemon, where Rastko should abide till the days of his learning were at an end and he might be blessed in the sacred brotherhood.

But after three days there came riding to the mountain a band of warriors, with a prince's son at their head, and of all whom he encountered he made inquiry, saying: "Hast thou beheld my brother, a comely youth, gold-haired and clad in a prince's golden garb, who came this way in company of three agèd monks?"

And at length one answered him, saying: "Such a youth have I seen, radiant as a wingèd seraph, and he hath taken refuge in the Lavra of Saint Pantelemon."

And the warriors hastened to Saint Pantelemon, whose twelve towers rise in beauty beside the blue sea, and dismounting from their steeds, they entered into the court where a black monk greeted them, crying: "God keep you in health, ye weary travelers! What seek ye within our portals?"

And Vukan answered him: "The treasure ye have stolen from my sire."

And the monk said: "Speak gently, noble youth, for here dwell the meek servants of our Saviour, and no brigand horde."

And Vukan cried in wrath: "Yet ye took from the hands of Nemanya treasure and gold for a service ye rendered not, and from his breast his well-belovèd son."

Now in that moment Rastko, whose prayers had been troubled by the sound of his brother's voice, came forth into the sunlight and looked upon the face of Vukan and said: "From the heart of my father none may tear his son save my father alone. And for the treasure, say to him who sent thee that even the holy Patriarch, when hungry, will steal a crust of bread. Moreover, the gold we have taken from his store

49

weighs as naught in the balance against the treasure I shall lay up in heaven for him and all his seed."

But Vukan answered: "What thou hast to tell him, let him hear from thine own lips, for thou shalt return with us." And unmindful of Nemanya's behest, he commanded his warriors to fall upon Rastko and take him captive.

Then the youth, seeing that he might in no wise resist their onslaught, cried: "I will go with thee in peace, my brother, on the morrow, when I have bade farewell to those who befriended me, and prayed forgiveness of God Whom I forsake to please my sire. But lay not thy hands in violence upon me, else shalt thou rue the deed, as I am a prince and equally with thee son of the mighty Nemanya."

And Vukan answered: "So be it," and departed out of that place.

But Rastko went straightway to the ancient higumen who ruled over Pantelemon, and kneeling before him, cried: "My father, receive me this night, I entreat thee, into thy holy covenant, for Nemanya hath sent his messengers to take me captive, and I know no refuge save in the arms of God."

And the agèd man blessed him, saying: "Let His will be done." And through the night they knelt together before the altar, praying that His grace might descend upon the head of His servant Rastko.

And before the dawn, the black brothers of Pantelemon came by two and two into the church with lighted tapers, and chanting the holy office, they shore from the head of Rastko his golden hair and took the

50

golden garments from his body, and clad him in the habit of a monk. And the ancient higumen signed him with the sign of the Cross to God's service, saying: "Thou shalt be called Rastko no longer, for Sava I baptize thee in the name of the Father and of the Son and of the Holy Ghost."

And when the office was ended, there sounded a loud tumult in the court, and the voice of Vukan clamored at the portal: "Open, lest we shatter your church into fragments and your heads as well."

And the portal being opened, the black monks issued forth by two and two, and when Vukan saw that his brother was not among them, he dashed into their midst, scattering them to right and left, and with drawn sword would have entered the holy habitation of God to profane its sanctity.

But the ancient higumen, who had followed after his children, raised his staff against the breast of Vukan, and spoke sternly, saying: "Take not this sin upon thy soul, thou arrogant man, for who will wash thee clean of it on the Judgment Day?"

And Vukan, who might not curb his hasty spirit, cried: "I will answer for my sins when God summons me, nor pray for quarter. But do thou, O venerable one, look to the sins of thy servants who for my father's kindness robbed him of his treasure, and of Rastko, his son."

But ere the holy father could make answer to the taunting of Vukan, a voice cried from above: "Rastko is dead, but Sava liveth in the Lord." And looking aloft, Vukan beheld, high in the tower above him, the face of Sava the monk, he who had been his brother Rastko. And Sava let fall a sack at the feet of Vukan and cried: "That which is left of Nemanya's youngest son lies at thy feet. Take it to him who was my father, and say that I send him gold for gold and this word in farewell: if he weep for me, the Lord will dry his tears; but if for his lost treasure, there is no power in heaven or earth to comfort him."

And the glory that moved about the head of Sava smote Vukan to earth, and when he raised his eyes again, his brother was vanished from the tower and the monks from the court, and he stood alone among his warriors who for wonder might not move neither hand nor foot. Then he took up the sack that lay at his feet, and went forth from that house of peace wherein he had wrought strife, and his people followed after him. And mounting their steeds, they returned to Rashka.

And entering the chamber where Nemanya awaited them, Vukan bowed before him and delivered up unto him the sack flung from the tower of Saint Pantelemon by the hand of Sava, and he said: "Rastko is dead, but Sava liveth in the Lord, and he bids me say that he sends thee gold for gold and this word in farewell: if thou weep for him, the Lord will dry thy tears; but if for thy lost treasure, there is no power in heaven or earth to comfort thee."

And with his dagger Nemanya slit the belly of the sack, and lo! there fell upon his knees the golden hair of Rastko, and the golden tunic that had clasped his body, and the golden shoes of his feet, and in love and sorrow his father laid his hands upon them.

Then raising his scepter, he cried: "Let the court and all who cherished Rastko, my son, be garbed in black, and for the space of thirty days let his death be mourned. But when the time of mourning is ended, rejoice ye and be glad that the house of Nemanya hath given a saint unto God!"

And when the days of mourning were ended, the Grand Zhupan sent gifts to Athos, of wine and steeds and cattle, of samite and jeweled robes, and to Sava he sent his blessing. And from that day forward, he saw clearly the vanity of life, that is as the passing away of smoke, and early and late he besought God's grace on his soul till, purged of sin, it lay sweetly within his breast, like a vessel uplifted to receive the Sacrament.

Then he called together his nobles and high churchmen, they who sat in the Sabor, and he named Vukan, his first-born, prince in Zeta, denying him his birthright, lest the breath of his rude spirit lay its blight over all the land. But his throne and scepter he gave into the keeping of Stefan, who was made in his father's image. And he said: "Behold, in the name of the Lord, I raise up this my son to rule in my stead the state entrusted to me by God and your love. And I pray you, give him your kindness and your faith as to me ye have given them."

53

faithful monks and seized its wealth and, sailing away, had flung into its heart a fiery brand that consumed it utterly.

And Simeon said: "Let us rear it anew, my son, with stouter walls and loftier towers and altars more richly decked, that it may bear everlasting witness to the love of Nemanya's house for our blessèd Lord Jesus, and shine as a torch in the night to welcome our people who would flee to its sanctuary."

And Stefan sent them silver and gold to their need, and they reared fair Hilandar anew with stouter walls and loftier towers and altars more richly decked, and against the walls many cells were built to house the holy, and the church rose in their midst, adorned with holy images and crowned with four domes that bore the emblem of Christ, and floored with bright marbles. And it was blessèd in the name of the Coming of the Mother of God to the Temple.

And on fair parchment, sealed with his golden seal, Simeon wrote: "This Lavra of Hilandar do I give, out of the love I bear them, to my Serbian people, that they may name me in their prayers forever, me and my sons and my sons' sons to unending generations. And if any lay hands in malice hereon, let him be curst with all the pains of hell by Jesus Christ, our Lord, and His blessèd Mother, and by me, His servant, who hath striven to follow in His footsteps."

And from thenceforward Hilandar hath been known as the Serbian Lavra on Athos, giving shelter to all who knock in need on its portals.

It came to pass that the weight of his years lay heavy on Simeon's head, and knowing that the hour of his far voyage was at hand, he spoke unto Sava, saying: "When my soul is fled, let my sinful body be borne to the land of my people and buried in Studenitsa." And having bade farewell to his brethren, he said: "Make ready, I pray you, a pallet of straw in the church and a pillow of stone, and bring me thither, that mine eyes may rest on the face of the Mother of God."

And they made ready a pallet of straw in the church and a pillow of stone, and brought him thither, and peace lay upon his brow as his eyes rested on the face of the Mother of God. And Sava sat beside him and read from the Holy Book the words of the Psalmist: "Keep me, O God, for I have taken refuge in Thee. I have no good but in Thee. Thou art my rock and my fortress and my deliverer, my shield and my horn of salvation, my high tower. I will praise the Lord while I live. I will sing praises unto my God while I have my being."

And Simeon answered: "Amen. Let all things that have breath praise the Lord," and yielded up his soul and died.

Black broke the day of Simeon's death over the Serbian land, black and bitter because of the wrath of Vukan, whose birthright had been given to his brother. For while Nemanya lived, he held secret his discontent, to kneel in homage at the feet of the Tsar Feodor Laska and Manuel, his Patriarch. And they received him kindly and said unto him: "We would give proof of our love to thee and to thy brother, the right-believing Stefan. Now say what gift we may bestow upon you that will gladden your hearts."

And Sava answered: "My lords, we lack neither of gold nor silver, and your love is a greater treasure than aught else ye may bestow. Yet if ye would bring gladness indeed to our hearts and strength to the church, hear ye the boon we crave. Well do ye know how the land is corrupted with heresies and evil doctrine, and only by divine mercy have we upheld the banner of truth among our people. Now if ye would lighten our task, let Stefan be crowned king, for what the Grand Zhupan hath rendered in service to God, the King may render tenfold. Moreover, the way is long from Rashka, and troubled by warring princes, and many pitfalls beset his feet who would journey hither. Wherefore, I pray you, grant us of your grace an archbishop in Serbia, to crown her kings and rule over her churchmen and be subject to none save the Patriarch alone."

And of their grace they granted this boon unto Sava and the Serbian land, and in the presence of the Tsar and all his court and the synod, Manuel the Patriarch blessed Sava to be Archbishop in Serbia, investing him with the miter and the shepherd's staff. And the Tsar gave into his hands the crown of a king, that he might crown his brother.

Now there was great rejoicing when he returned in his new-made glory to Ras, and Stefan commanded that a church be built to be named the church of the Archbishop, with cloisters and green gardens for his delight. And at the feast of the Lord's Ascension, the Grand Zhupan, with Radoslav, his first-born, and his nobles, and the bishops and priests of the realm, a mighty multitude, assembled within the church. And Stefan knelt down before the altar, and Sava prayed God's blessing upon him, and anointed him with the holy oil and the balm, and laid the purple robe about his shoulders, and gave into his hand the scepter of power and crowned him with Nikaea's crown. And he cried unto the people: "He that hath been your Grand Zhupan is now your King. Long life to Stefan, first-crowned King of the Serbs!"

And they bowed down before him, crying: "Hail to our King! Long life to Stefan First-Crowned!"

So Stefan was crowned King, and the house of Nemanya, being glorified, shed glory over all the land, and Serbia grew in pride among the nations of the earth. Yet, alas, though nations live, their kings must pass away into the tomb, and so it chanced that in the fullness of time Stefan lay sick unto death. And he spoke to those who were gathered about him, but so faint was his voice that they must needs bend low their ears to hear. And he said: "Let Sava come and

And after many moons she was healed of her hurts, yet nevermore did she reveal her face to the light of day, but went veiled in darkness. And behind the walls of Saint Demetrios, Radoslav beat his breast and prayed without ceasing for the soul of his lost Queen. And his people forgot that he had been their sovereign, and named him the mad monk Yovan.

I N THE reign of Vladislav, Sava, returning from his pilgrimage to the Holy Land, came to the city of Turnovo where he sickened and died. And the King journeyed thither, and bore his body again to Serbia that their saint might lie among the people he had loved. And he slept in the Lord beneath the stones of Mileshevo till the day when our land was oppressed by the infidel, and Sinan Pasha, may his name be forever accurst in the Judgment Book, burned his sacred bones, thinking thus to destroy the power of the Wonder-Maker. Yet little did he know of God's goodness to those who serve Him, for the virtue that lay within his relics escaped the flames, and still doth our father walk among his children, bringing heart to their weariness, and to their desolation, hope.

Neither into his eldest nor his second-born passed the soul of Stefan First-Crowned, for Vladislav trembled before the onslaught of the Golden Horde, and yielded the kingdom to the care of Urosh his brother, yet thou didst name me vassal, commanding my hosts as they had been thine own. Therefore I turned against thee."

"King art thou, yet not my peer, but my chainèd captive, subject to my command as the thrall that lays his neck beneath my foot."

And Urosh cried in anguish: "My son hath betrayed me, else hadst thou not put me to shame."

But Bela answered: "Thou hast betrayed thy son, else had he not sought aid against thee. He is thy first-born, destined by God to follow after thee. Art thou belike God's peer to dispute His decree?"

Then Urosh could not choose but humble himself before Bela, pledging his word that Dragutin thenceforward should share his throne and realm, being named the younger King, and should rule alone after his father's death.

And the Grecian Princess, daughter to Mihailo, having set forth with joy and gifts and silken banners for Rashka, must needs return again to Tsarigrad, unwed and woebegone.

And Urosh, returning in bitterness of heart to his kingdom, called the Sabor together, and summoned his son Dragutin to appear before him, and said: "My lords and brothers, we have sworn to the Magyar that Dragutin shall share our throne and realm while yet we live, being named the younger King, and shall rule after our death. And we have bowed the head before Bela, and the King's banner rests among his trophies as the sign of our downfall. And these things are come to pass through the treachery of this my son."

Then Dragutin spoke, saying: "Not treachery, my father, but the will to keep what is mine own, which thou unjustly wouldst have given to my brother."

And the Sabor decreed that, under the seal of the King, Dragutin should rule the land from Dubrovnik to Skadar's Lake and from the Black Drin to the sea. And all was written down on fair parchment by the hand of Danilo the monk, he who became Archbishop in Serbia.

Yet for many months Urosh withheld his seal from the decree, and Bela died, and Ladislaus was King, and Milutin took to wife the daughter of the great Sebastocrat in Thessaly.

And still his oath was unfulfilled that Urosh had sworn to the Magyar, and the Prince tarried unwilling in his father's house, and hatred each of the other consumed them.

But at length, on that day when their lord was wont to give ear to the plaints of his people, Dragutin knelt before the throne and cried: "I sue for justice."

And Urosh answered: "Who hath injured thee?"

And he said: "Thou, sire! The land that lies from Dubrovnik to Skadar's lake and from the Black Drin to the sea is mine by the faith of a king and the Sabor's decree. How long wilt thou withhold it from me?"

Then the King rose up in his anger and cried: "Till my strength be spent, and my word an idle breath. Shall I reward thy sins and give thee lands for the evil thou gavest me?"

And Dragutin cried: "So be it!" and went from the chamber, and went from his father's house, and rode

to Matchva where Ladislaus, his kinsman, had arrayed
an army of Magyars and Tartars to await his command.
And he led them against his sire who, all unready for
combat, marshaled as best he might his warriors, and
in the mountains of Gacko joined battle with his rebel
son. And from dawn to dark the conflict raged between them, favoring now the King, now Dragutin,
and many a sin did the Prince take on his soul, slaying his countrymen. Yet dark are the ways of the
Lord, and by men not to be fathomed, for ere night fell
He gave the victory to him who, defying his father,
had transgressed the law brought down from Sinai's
mount. And Urosh, in terror for his life, took flight
to Humlie, ending his days a monk, but Dragutin
marched upon Ras and subdued the city and proclaimed himself King over the Serbs.

Yet brief was his trimph, for well the wise man
knows that if God take not His reckoning today, on
the morrow He will take more abundant measure.

And so it chanced that the King, riding at morn
among his nobles by the stronghold of Yeletch, uttered
suddenly a fearsome cry and let fall the reins, and his
steed, affrighted, galloped like one scourged of demons
and flung his master to earth, where he lay bereft of all
sense. And being borne to the castle, for many days
Azrael sat beside him but put not forth his hand, awaiting the judgment of the Giver of Life and Death. And
God weighed in the balance the deeds of Dragutin,

70

then spoke to His angel, saying: "For the sake of Saint Simeon and Saint Sava, who kneel in supplication before my throne, let him live that his soul may be redeemed." And the Angel of Death folded his wings about him and went his way.

So Dragutin was healed, but lo! when he would have set his foot to the ground, it upheld him not, and he walked, not as a King but as a halting beggar bayed by hounds. And his proud soul sickened, and he hid himself from the sight of his household, fearing their scorn. And he cried in his heart: "O Lord, Thou Lord of Justice, mine eyes that were blinded see, my heart that was hard is as water beneath thy touch. Because I lifted my hand against my father, hast Thou laid this heavy burden upon me. I have done evil, God. Take pity upon me. I am a sinner. Do Thou pardon me."

And that the All-Merciful might know he had repented truly, he summoned Milutin, his brother, and said unto him: "Now shalt thou hear what none beside thee hath heard. As I rode among my nobles by the fortress of Yeletch, my father appeared unto me, not in his guise as he lived, but with pallid flesh, like one new-risen from the grave. And thrice he spoke unto me, saying: 'Prepare thyself to die,' and being sore afraid, I cried aloud and fell from my steed. Yet I was healed of my sickness and rejoiced, thinking that my sin had been forgiven unto me, but alas! God hath broken my body as a sign to me that I am no longer King. Wherefore take thou the kingdom, my brother, and rule wisely over thy people. God grant thee years, and Christ defend thee against the wiles of

71

Satan, and the Holy Ghost uplift thee upon his wings. And if thou wouldst requite the gift, pray that my soul may be saved from the river of fire and Gehenna's torments, for I fear them, my brother, and in all the world there is no spot where I may hide my face away from them."

And Milutin answered: "Be of good cheer, my King. Whom the Lord loves He chastens, and surely He had not spared thy life to damn thy soul. And for the land, if it be thy will to yield it unto me, with God's help I will rule."

And Dragutin gave unto his brother his steed and armor, and the sword that hung on his thigh, and departed with his wife and Vladislav, his son, to Matchva, where his Magyar kinsman had bestowed broad lands upon him. And there he lived the years of his life in penitence and prayer, and there in the peace of the church he died.

Now Milutin was beloved of heaven, and the land flowered beneath his sway, and the people multiplied, and the earth put forth her fruits. And in all the world no wheat grew so tall as the yellow wheat of Prizren, and no gold was so bright as the gold from the mountains of Banska, and no holy books so graciously adorned as by the hand of Athos' monks, and no church more fit to be God's dwelling-place than the church of the Archbishop at white Pyetch.

And it chanced that the king journeyed to Beograd

to take counsel with his brother, and beheld in the castle Yelisava, the nun, she who was sister to the Queen. And at night he entered in to her chamber and lay with her, though she wept, for she had known no man before him. And for many nights thereafter he went in to her, and when she was with child, he put from him the Grecian Princess he had taken out of Thessaly, she who had borne him his son Constantine, and took Yelisava to wife.

But the people murmured against him, that one who had vowed herself to the Lord should share his throne, and the Archbishop Danilo admonished him, saying: "Thou hast sinned, my son. Yet if thou wilt repent, forsaking this woman, God will bless thee in the seed of a holier marriage."

And Milutin hearkened to his words, and sent Yelisava from him to the cloister on the Island of the Hare, where in due time she was shriven of her fault, and God called her to be mother over her sisters, whom she ruled with a strong hand. And Milutin took in marriage the Lady Yula, daughter to the Bulgar Tsar, who bare him Stefan.

Know, my children, that the King was a mighty warrior, stout branch of a stout root, and his name struck terror to the bowels of his enemies, and they fled before him. And from the Greeks he seized the white city of Skoplie, and many strongholds beside yielded themselves to his prowess. And when Shishman, Prince of Viddin, rose up against him, and with the aid of thrice-accursèd Tartars strove to plunder our holy church at Pyetch, Milutin drove him back with blows so fierce that he fled in dismay beyond the Danube, whence presently he sent his messengers to sue for mercy. And Milutin was moved to grant his suit, and gave his daughter Nada to be wedded to Mihailo, Shishman's son. And the Bulgar princess Feodora he took to be Stefan's wife, and Stefan was his regent over Zeta, and over Humlie, Constantine.

Thus, having subdued his foe on every hand and ordered his household, he gave thanks to the Lord, crying: "For that Thou hast preserved me, and crushed mine adversaries under Thy heel, I will praise Thee, O God. And for each year Thou dost grant me to abide in life, I will build Thee a church and sacred dwellings where men shall exalt Thy name."

And God was pleased with the vow of Milutin, and granted him yet forty years of life, that he might fulfill his oath. And he built forty churches, fair as the castles of a king, and he strengthened them with high towers and adorned them with vessels of silver and of gold, and bestowed upon them forests and orchards and fruitful vineyards, that they might serve the Lord with bounty. And he tore down the church of Hilandar, raising anew in yet greater splendor that torch of the Nemanyas, that star of Athos.

So for many years he dwelt in the grace of heaven till, alas, there came to him an envoy from the Grecian Tsar, saying: "Andronicus, my master, hath a fair young daughter, a bud unblossomed, a tender sapling that hath not yet put forth her first green shoot. Wilt thou take her, great King, that there may be friendship

74

between us and peace on our borders? And for the Lady Yula, let her rest content since, if it be thy will, the Despot Andrey, kinsman to the Tsar, will espouse her with the blessing of holy church. And the land thou hast taken from us by the sword shall be doubly thine by reason of this covenant."

And Milutin sealed a covenant with the Greek, and sent heralds throughout his kingdom to proclaim his purpose. And he said: "I have sinned, for I took the Lady Yula to wife, while Yelisava lived and she who was the mother of Constantine. But when mine eyes were opened to the evil I had wrought, heavy with sorrow, I poured ashes upon my head, and rent my garments and fell at the feet of God till He spoke to me, saying: 'Before thou hast left the bed of thy corruption thou shalt not be cleansed.' And straightway I left her bed with whom I had lain in guilt, and God pardoned me. Yet the King may not lie alone, so, taking thought for the welfare of my people, I have sealed a covenant with the Greek, our ancient foe. And the Lady Yula shall be joined in holy wedlock with Andrey the Despot, but Simonide, daughter to the Tsar, shall be your Queen as a pledge of friendship between us and everlasting peace upon our borders. And the land we have won by the sword shall be doubly ours by reason of this covenant."

And many rose up against Milutin who were loath to seal a covenant with the Greek, and many who loved the Lady Yula upbraided him, and Stefan her son, he who was Prince in Zeta, reviled his father, by whose

75

will he had been dishonored. But Milutin, desirous of the maid, heeded them not.

Then from Tsarigrad Andronicus rode forth in splendor with all his court, and camels went before them, laden with silks and sweet-smelling perfumes and carpets from the looms of Araby, and elephants followed after, with precious gifts of silver and of gold. And in their midst, high on the shoulders of forty blackamoors, was borne the litter of Simonide.

And they journeyed till they came to Vardar's shore, on whose farther bank Milutin, among his nobles, awaited them. And hostages were given and received, and the Lady Yula was carried across the waters and delivered up to the Greeks.

Then Simonide, pride of her father's court, was brought forth from her litter. Slight was her stature as the stature of a child, but for her countenance, nine veils of silver veiled it from the eyes of men. And her head rose proud beneath her golden crown, and her robe was thick with jewels like the robe of the Holy Mother of our Lord, and about her throat nine jeweled necklets hung, and her feet were shod in pearls. And the Tsar, her father, took her white hand in his and placed her within the barque that bore her to the farther shore. And Milutin received her, and lifted the silver veils that veiled her face, and smiled upon her, for she was fair as the crescent moon. But the maiden trembled, standing like a doe affrighted by the sound of the hunter's horn in the deep forest. And suddenly she turned and fled from beneath the hand of Milutin ere he could stay her flight, and cast herself into Vardar's rushing stream. But Nogai, the Tartar, sped after her, and plunging into the waters, drew her forth again and laid her at his master's feet.

And Milutin cried: "The maid is weary, having journeyed far. Let her be taken to the palace, and softly bedded, and comforted with fruits and rosy wine, and let sweet music lull her to rest. And do thou, Nogai, keep watch beside her, and if harm befall her, the service thou hast rendered me heretofore shall be as naught, and thy life shall pay the penalty."

Then Simonide was borne away, and the Greeks, who had feared the wrath of the King, rejoiced mightily, and having crossed the Vardar, were welcomed with honor and acclaim in white Skoplie.

And on the morrow the young Grecian maid knelt beside her lord in the church he had reared to the holy Constantine, and the Serbian Archbishop blessed them in the bonds of wedlock. And returning to the castle, they feasted for seven days, and the guslars sang of Simonide's beauty and the glory of Milutin; and of the splendor of the Greeks they sang, and of the solemn covenant sealed between them, bringing peace and abundance. And when the feast was ended and rich gifts had been bestowed upon them, the guests bade farewell to their Princess, and took their way again to Tsarigrad. And the Lady Yula went among them to be Andrey's bride.

77

Now Simonide was to the Serbian King as the light of his eyes, dearer than his sons and more to be desired than great treasure. But she looked coldly upon him, for he was full of years and had plucked her unready from the bough, and she went in heaviness to his bed and left it with joy. Yet, though she bore him no sons, he chided her not, but thinking to please her, said: "If thy womb be barren, still shall the seed of thy fathers rule on my throne, for I will divide my land among thy brothers, if thou wilt but love me, Simonide."

Yet she was moved neither by kindness nor anger to cherish him, and when he laid his hand upon her she suffered him, but gave not her own in love.

Now it chanced one day that the Lady Simonide walked with her maidens in the pleasant gardens of the King, and came upon Stefan, his son, who would have bowed before her and gone his way, but she stayed him, bidding her maidens withdraw, and spoke to him, saying: "Vainly dost thou spend thy hatred upon me, thou son of the King. Not I, but the sire that begot thee, is thy foe and except thou look to it, thou who wert born a prince shalt die a beggar." And having spoken, she called to her maidens, who gathered the hem of her garment from the grass and her flowing sleeves, and so she departed from the sight of Stefan.

But now his heart, that had been turned against his father, was eaten as by vipers. And he withdrew to Zeta, where many noble lords of the realm came to him secretly, feeding his bitterness and nursing the

78

seed of strife between sire and son, till it was grown to a mighty tree. And they said: "Do thou lead us against this lover of the Greeks who hath named thee bastard, and we will restore to thee the throne whereof he would rob thee and thy children's children to enrich our foe." And he hearkened unto their counsel, conspiring with them to destroy his father, and all the chieftains and voyevodas rallied to his standard, and Milutin was left unfriended.

Yet, though he was forsaken of his warriors and braved by him to whom he had given life, he despaired not, but sent his messengers to Athos and to the river Banska, to Treskevatz and domed Grachanitsa, and to all the cloisters and holy places he had reared to God. And he said: "Give me again, I pray you, of the treasure wherewith I heaped your coffers in kinder days, and having served my need, it shall be returned to you in full measure, pressed down and overflowing."

And the monks heard his prayer, and gathered together the treasure of their coffers and their carven vessels and the garments, pearl-embroidered, wherein they worshiped the Lord, and blessing the gift, they sent it to Milutin. And the King summoned before him the merchants of Venice and proud Dubrovnik, and bartered the treasure for golden ducats that he might buy fierce fighters among the Turks, and among the Tartars, horsemen. And having assembled a goodly host, he rode forth from white Skoplie to do battle with his son Stefan.

But when the Nemanyitch learned that his sire, at the head of a mighty army, advanced against him, he

79

that had been stiff-necked and full of pride grew sick at heart, and having crossed the Boyana, he kept within his tent, nor would he take counsel with his chieftains nor lay his commands upon them.

And after three days he dispatched to the camp of Milutin his servant Franyo, who prostrated himself at the feet of the angry King and spoke in this wise: "My master bids me say he doth repent him of his wickedness, whereunto he hath been moved by the counsel of evildoers and the enemies of my lord. But if thou wilt pledge thine honor for his life, he will lay down his arms, yielding himself to thy mercy, mighty King, for he is sick at heart and may not be healed save by the balm of thy forgiveness."

And Milutin answered: "Let him withdraw his troops beyond the stream, and send me in chains those evildoers and enemies of the King who have moved him against me, and let him follow me, unarmed, unshod, and in the sackcloth of repentance to white Skoplie. Mine honor for his life, if he do these things according to my command. If not, by the living Mother of God I swear he shall perish on his father's sword."

And Franyo bore the words of the King to his lord Stefan, who withdrew his troops beyond the stream and caused his father's enemies to be bound and brought in chains before him. And looking upon them, Milutin cried: "Let their heads be stricken from their shoulders, and borne on the spears of my Tartars to white Skoplie, for thus should men perish who might have

80

served a lion, yet chose a hare instead to be their master."

And the chieftain Voyina lifted his neck, bowed down with fetters, and answered: "Thy words are just as thy name is glorious, sire. Yet who could have said that a lion's cub might be transformed to a hare?"

And when Milutin turned again to the east, the heads of his enemies were borne before him on Tartar spears, and behind him followed his son Stefan, unarmed save for his sword that trailed in the dust, unshod and heavy with the burden of iron chains upon his vanquished neck. And the people mocked him and cast stones upon him, till his body was red with wounds as his bleeding feet.

N HIS golden hall Milutin sat in judgment, surrounded by his priests and councilors, and the fair Simonide sat beside him. And Stefan, his son, lay prostrate at his feet and cried: "Mercy, my father, by the hour of my begetting! Mercy, as thou dost hope for mercy before God's throne!"

And Milutin answered: "Not I, but the Sabor, hath pronounced judgment upon thee. And they have decreed that because thou hast treacherously raised thy hand against the King, thou shalt be cast to earth and with hot irons robbed of the sight of thine eyes. And thou shalt be banished to the country of the Greeks, together with Feodora, thy wife, and thy two young sons. Yet I, thy father, am loath to carry out this judgment upon thee, and if it please the Queen to sue for thy pardon, I will give ear to her plea. Speak, Simonide."

And the Queen looked down upon Stefan where he lay at her feet and, smiling a smile of scorn, she cried: "What need of his eyes hath a coward that dare not look upon the light of the sun? Let him go in darkness with the earthworm who is his brother! Let him be blinded! I will not sue for him."

Then a bitter cry broke from the lips of Stefan: "Slay me, my father, though thou didst pledge thine honor for my life, but blind me not."

And Milutin sealed his ears to the prayer of his son, and raising his scepter, cried: "Do with him as the Sabor hath decreed."

And four stout Vlachs bound the unhappy prince both hand and foot, and bore him to a dungeon in the bowels of the earth and with hot irons burned out his eyes. And so great were the pains of his flesh that he might not with patience endure them, but screamed as a beast screams in the wilderness, whom the hunter's arrow hath wounded, yet not slain. Then God took pity upon him and made numb his senses, and for three days and nights he lay as though in the arms of death, knowing neither fear nor sorrow. And on the third night our holy Sava appeared unto him, and laid his hands in compassion upon his brow, and spoke softly, saying: "Grieve not, my son. Thine eyes are in my keeping." And Stefan was comforted.

So for many years thereafter, the blind Nemanyitch abode in Tsarigrad with his faithful wife, Feodora, and his two young sons, Dushan and Dushitsa. And for a space he dwelt in the palace of Andronicus, who loved him well, but alas! the hand of God smote him once more, sending a fever to consume the fair child

Dushitsa that languished and died. And when the days of his mourning were at an end, Stefan sought leave of Andronicus to depart from that place, saying: "The Lord is angered that I, who should weep in sackcloth and chasten my sinful body with lean fare, have taken mine ease amid the pleasures of thy court, O Basileus. Suffer me therefore to do penance in some narrow cell, lest He smite anew and my burden be greater than I can bear."

And the Tsar commended him to the brothers of Pantakrator who received him kindly and led him in the angel way of life, that he knew not Feodora nor any woman. And for his continence God pardoned his sin, and he was at peace.

Not so Milutin, his father, rich in glory and pleasure, but unquiet that he had blinded his son, and hungering for the love of Simonide that she gave him not. And now he besought her, and now he poured over her shining head the vials of his wrath, yet still she turned from him in hatred, mocking his desire, and he that had been a king was become a slave to stand watch above her, lest she yield to another what she denied her lord.

And it came to pass that Irene, mother to Simonide, sickened and died, and the Queen must needs journey to Tsarigrad to mourn beside her bier. Yet Milutin might not bear her company, having arrayed his hosts to do battle against the Magyar King. Wherefore he gave Simonide into the hands of Nogai the Tartar, saying: "Let thine eyes cover her by day, and by night do thou lie across her threshold."

And Simonide journeyed to Tsarigrad, but Milutin led his forces against the Magyar and vanquished him, returning to white Skoplie with the prizes of war. And his heart beat high with hope, for he thought: "Lo! I come as a victor, bearing rich gifts, and the Queen cannot choose but welcome me with thanksgiving and joy." And truly the King was welcomed with joy and thanksgiving, yet neither his lady, nor Nogai the Tartar, nor any among those who had journeyed to Tsarigrad, came forth to do him honor. And he cried in vexation of spirit: "Where is my lady and the Tartar Nogai and those that journeyed with them to Tsarigrad, that they come not forth to welcome the King?"

And the master of his household, kneeling before him, answered: "Let mine ears be severed from my head, O Serbia's sun, for I have sent many messengers to Constantine's golden city by the sea, who have returned to me, saying: 'The Queen weeps for her mother's death and may not leave the palace of the Tsar'; and again, 'The Queen makes a pilgrimage to the shrine of the Blessèd Virgin, where she will pray for the peace of her mother's soul'; and yet again, 'She is returned in weariness from her pilgrimage, and must seek repose ere she journey to white Skoplie.' Thus have I done, and thus have I been answered, O shield of thy people! Lay thou thy command upon me!"

And Milutin bade him send again to Tsarigrad,

saying: "Let Simonide, whether she weep or laugh, weary in spirit or restored to strength, in health or sickness, leave her father's palace straightway for the palace of her lord. And if she linger, he will come at the head of his hosts who lust for blood, having routed the Magyar hordes, and they will destroy the city of Tsarigrad, and slay the Tsar in the midst of his golden court, and take Simonide captive, leading her back in shame to white Skoplie that she left with honor."

And the messenger bore the words of Milutin to Andronicus, whom they affrighted, and he cried: "Let my daughter be brought before me to hear her lord's command."

But he that was dispatched to her chamber returned to the Tsar, and knelt before him crying: "Thy pardon, Basileus! The Queen lies faint upon her couch, and for heaviness may not lift up her head."

Then the Tsar rose up in wrath from his golden throne and went through the halls and gardens of his palace, till he was come to the chamber of Simonide, where he entered in. And she lay amid bright silks, as a pearl lies in a ring of burning gold, and with the plumes of peacocks her maidens stirred the air to coolness, and Nogai the Tartar stood at the head of her couch, his arms crossed over his breast.

But Andronicus hardened his heart against her, remembering the words of Milutin, and he cried: "Think no more to deceive me, my daughter, for well I know thou art not sick save with hatred of thy lord, whereof none but thyself may heal thee. And thou shalt set forth straightway for white Skoplie, whither

86

Milutin is returned in triumph from Matchva, angered to find thee still absent from his bed. And if thou linger, he will descend upon us to slay me with all my court, and thou, who art loath to bend thy neck before God, shall be dragged in shame back to thy husband's arms."

And she answered: "Who am I that I should oppose thee, my father, or kindle against thee the wrath of my gentle lord! Let the caravan be prepared, that I may hasten homeward to gladden his eyes. Yea, and in proof of my love, ere I depart I will visit his erring son at Pantakrator for whom he grieves, and bring him tidings of his welfare."

And the Tsar was well content with her reply, and sent her on the morrow, under the care of a pious monk and the Tartar Nogai, to visit Pantakrator, that she might speak with Stefan and bring to his father tidings of his welfare. And the higumen received her, and led her to a vaulted chamber, where presently the Prince came in to her, an oaken staff in his hand, and a cloth of linen bound over his eyes.

And he said: "Wherefore art thou come to me?"

And she answered: "To look upon thee, and to learn if thou have some message for thy sire, who grieves for his son."

"Say to him that my soul is filled with light as mine eyes with darkness, and his grief is a sin against the Lord."

"And art thou grown so godly, Stefan, that thou canst no longer hate?"

"Truly the Lord hath banished hatred from my

heart, else should I hate none so well as thee, Simonide."

"Yet I am thy friend, and would help thee to thy kingdom as once in the gardens at Skoplie I strove to help thee. What though thine eyes be dark? Thou shalt see with mine, and by the light of thy wisdom shalt thou guide me."

"Not in kindness art thou come hither, black Satan's fiend, but to rob me of my peace. Wherefore begone, lest I forget the patience I have learned within these walls and do thee hurt."

"What hurt canst thou do me greater than that thou hast already done, blind fool Stefan, blinder when thy black eyes burned in thy head than now thou art. Was I not fairer to look upon than thy meek Feodora? Did I not point thee the way to glory, and thou who hadst but to reach forth thy hand and seize her garment, must fall a-trembling and weep and turn thy humble back to thy father's rod. Say, dost thou cower still, Stefan, or hast thou learned in this proud land to go upright as Grecian princes go?"

And Stefan, within whose breast a tempest raged, might rule it no longer, and raising his staff, he would have struck Simonide to earth, yet his blind arm found her not, and she laughed to see him smite a shadow, crying: "Truly, thou art grown valorous, for to belabor thy foe, though she be a woman, is better than to trail thy sword in the dust."

Then Stefan drew from his breast the sacred cross and, kissing it, cried: "May God's staff smite thee, whom my arm cannot reach! May thy womb be barren! Yet if thou bear a child, may he bring thee sorrow and shame! May the days of thy life be a curse unto thee and thy nights a torment, and when in the bitterness of thy pain thou dost cry on God, praying for death, may He show thee mercy as thou hast shown it me."

So he turned and left her, and Simonide laughed in her white throat, but wept in her heart.

And when her caravan was in readiness, she bade farewell to her father and her brothers and set forth for white Skoplie. And by day she was borne in a silken litter, and Nogai walked beside her, and by night she slept within a silken tent, on whose threshold Nogai lay.

And they came to Koprili, that was but a day's journey from the city of the King, as darkness hid the earth, and pitching their tents, they laid them down to rest. But ere she slumbered the Queen commanded rosy wine to be brought to her, and filled two chalices, and summoned Nogai the Tartar, crying: "Drink with me, Nogai! Drink with me to the morrow, whose happy feet shall lead us to our master. Drink with me, my friend and savior, that didst draw me from Vardar's waters to be a Queen, and sit upon a throne, and reign with my lord over a mighty people."

But Nogai cried: "I will not drink with thee, for thy pledge is false, and thou hast poisoned the cup." And dashing it to earth, he withdrew from the tent and laid him down to watch beside the threshold. And for an hour he watched, and for two and three, but in the end he slumbered. Yet God, who loved him for his faithful heart, sent an angel to stand guard above him, and at black midnight the wings of the angel brushed the Tartar's brow, and his voice cried: "Nogai, awake!"

And he awoke, and looked into the eyes of a black-clad nun, whose dagger was raised to strike. And he smote the dagger from her hand and flung it afar, and leaping to his feet, he tore from her body the garments wherein Simonide had thought to flee to the refuge of Saint Andreash. And she clung to his knees and besought him, crying: "Suffer me to depart in peace, good Nogai, and I will give thee my jewels and my store of gold and a swift steed to bear thee to the land of thy fathers where the King will never find thee. And thou shalt dwell like a prince in Tartary."

But he heeded her not, and summoned her maidens, and bade them garb her anew in the robes of a queen. And when she was appareled, they set forth again for white Skoplie that they reached with the setting sun. And Nogai gave the fair Simonide into the hands of his master, but of what was befallen on the road from Tsarigrad he spoke no word, lest the heart of the King be troubled.

Now when Stefan had dwelt for seven years in Pantakrator, he was stricken with a grievous malady,

90

and lay in anguish, crying on his father's name and on the pleasant places of his youth. And the leech of Andronicus, who ministered unto him, said: "Except he return to dwell in his father's house, he may not be healed."

Then did the Tsar in pity send his messenger to the Holy Mountain, even to the higumen of Hilandar did he send him, whom the King loved, and he said: "Stefan the Prince lies stricken of a grievous malady, and may not be healed save in his father's house. Do thou sue for him, since the King will not deny thee. Though the sin was grave, bitter hath the expiation been."

And the higumen journeyed from the Holy Mountain to the throne of Milutin, and sued for Stefan that he might return to dwell in the land of his fathers, and the King denied him not, saying: "Go thou and bring him hither!"

And Stefan was brought from the place of his exile to his father's house, together with Feodora and the young Dushan. And he was laid at the feet of Milutin who knew not his son, for his countenance was ravaged with much anguish and a cloth of linen was bound over his eyes. And Stefan spoke, and his voice was as the voice of a dying wind among branches, and he said: "I have sinned against thee, my father, and I have repented me of my sin. Do thou forgive me."

And the heart of Milutin smote him that he yearned over his son, and he went down from his throne and embraced him, and the tears of one bedewed the other's cheeks.

And Stefan dwelt in the house of his father till he

had been made whole, and when his strength was restored unto him, Milutin said: "I will give thee the valley of the Lim to be thy zhupa, and thou shalt rule over the land and her people, and none shall molest thee."

But the Prince answered: "Do not this thing unto me, my father, for I have lived so long with God that the cross is dearer to me than the scepter, and to pray more pleasant than to rule. Neither land nor people, but another boon do I crave of thy love. High on the face of a cliff that rises below thy holy city of Pyetch lies a secret cavern, where once Yovan the anchorite scourged his body of sin, till his soul, rejoicing, burst her mortal clay and fled to God. Thither would I go, though the way is bitter with fearsome passes and gorges that cleave the earth. Yet I know no fear, for the Lord will lead me by the hand to the mountaintop, and there where the bones of Yovan hallow the ground I will live as my master lived, that belike his spirit may enter into me and give me everlasting peace. And for my wife Feodora and the young Dushan, do thou take them into thy keeping, and God be with all."

And Milutin blessed the desire of his son, who went forth alone from Skoplie, his staff in his hand, and a cloth of linen bound over his eyes. And hungering, he prayed for alms, and being weary, laid him down to slumber by the roadside. And when he came to the church of Grachanitsa that his father had built, he entered in and offered thanksgiving to the Lord who had brought him so far upon his way. And when he came to Zvechan, one spoke to him, saying: "An evil day

will bring thee here again," and Stefan answered, "Let God's will be done," and journeyed farther.

And at length he reached Belai, the accursèd desert, and set his foot upon the mountain, and the Lord led him by the hand through fearsome passes and gorges that cleave the earth, and brought him in safety to the cavern of Yovan, high on the face of the cliff. And there he dwelt, so near to heaven that the clouds by day and the stars by night entered in at his door, and he heard no sound save the crying of eagles above, and below, the voice of the wild Bistritsa, striving without rest against the unholy spirit that troubles her waters.

And day followed upon night, and night upon day, and the seasons waxed and waned, and the years went by, till in a dream the blessèd Sava appeared to Stefan and said: "Thine hour is at hand, and this place shall know thee no more till thou come in thine earthly majesty to do honor to Him who is the Lord of lords and the King of kings."

In the fullness of his years, Milutin the King was gathered unto his fathers, having named his son Constantine to be his heir and ruler over all the Serbian realm and over Pomorye. And the people mourned him, for he had been to them a keen-edged sword against the foe, yet those there were who rejoiced that the weight of his hand had fallen from their necks. And the warriors he had brought from alien lands,

93

the Yassi and the Turks and Tartars, rose up against Constantine, whom they feared not, his words being stouter than his deeds, and they sacked the cities of Milutin and plundered his treasure, yea, even his churches did they despoil, spilling upon the sacred stones of God the blood of those who defended their altars. And when the King was borne in solemn state to Banska, they fell upon his body with oaths and mockery to defile it, and only by the help of God were they put to flight.

And seeing that no monarch, but a weakling, ruled on the throne, Vladislav, Dragutin's son, made war on his kinsman, and blood and desolation were over all the land of Serbia.

Then the nobles cried: "Let the Sabor be called together to make choice between these Princes ere, like wolves that have fallen on a single sheep, they rend the kingdom asunder."

And the warriors came from the battlefields and the bishops from their churches and monasteries, and assembled in the golden hall of the King at white Skoplie, to make choice of a ruler.

And the Princes Constantine and Vladislav appeared before them, and Constantine cried: "The kingdom is mine, by the word of my father Nemanya."

And Vladislav cried: "The kingdom is mine, first-born of the first-born."

And suddenly the portal was flung wide, and there entered in one who leaned on a staff, and a cloth of linen was bound over his eyes. And he cried: "Mine is the kingdom by the will of God and the wonder He hath wrought upon me! Behold, ye nobles and princes of the church! Behold and marvel! For I that have been blind am blind no longer!" And he tore the cloth from his head, and lo! his eyes that with hot irons had been seared to darkness now burned with light.

And those who beheld the wonder fell to their knees, yea, even they who had fought with Constantine and they whom Vladislav had named his friends, and with one voice they cried: "Hail, Stefan! Hail, chosen of God! Let Stefan be crowned!"

Thus was the outcast acclaimed, and he that had been stoned by his countrymen exalted to the high place of his forebears. And the youth Dushan, eagle of Serbia, was crowned beside his father as the younger King.

And naught troubled their reign till the Lady Feodora was drawn into the shadow of the tomb. And the people mourned her passing, for she had been a fair and pious queen, obedient to the will of God and Stefan the King. And he sorrowed for a space, then, as was fitting, took to his lonely bed Mara, daughter to the Paleolog, and of their union Symeon was born.

Now in Tsarigrad it came to pass that Andronicus the Elder must needs defend his realm against faithless nobles, moved by the younger Andronicus to defy

95

their rightful Tsar, and Stefan, remembering his deeds of lovingkindness, lent him aid and comfort. But he was betrayed by the master of his household who, when the moon was full, stole forth from the palace and opened the city gates to his enemy. And the ancient monarch was immured within the cloisters of Saint Phocas, and the younger Andronicus was Tsar.

And thinking how he might be avenged on Stefan, the new-made ruler bound unto him Mihailo, Shishman's son and Tsar over the Bulgars, and together they plotted woe on the heads of our people.

Mihailo the Tsar summoned into his presence the Lady Nada and spoke to her in this wise: "Thee and thy son do I banish from my love and kingdom. If ye be found after three days within my borders, ye shall surely die."

And Nada looked proudly upon him, though her heart like a cagèd falcon cried in her breast, and she said: "Wherein lies my fault against thee?"

And he answered: "In that thou art a Serb. Return to thy brother and say unto him: 'I am dishonored, and my son disowned and Mihailo will wed him with the sister of the Grecian Tsar. And leagued with his kinsman, he will come down upon thee to humble thee as our father humbled his, and his throne shall stand in thy halls.'"

And Nada answered him: "If it be God's will that

96

these things shall come to pass, let His will be done. And if thou wilt put me away for another, forgetting thy vows, though my heart cry out against the deed, it forgives the doer. But what of the child, my lord? A Serb is his mother, yet his sire is the Bulgar Tsar. And he is straight and comely, born of many princes, and in other days thou didst look fondly upon him, caressing his white brow and crying: 'Thou shalt be king of kings, my son.' Banish me, my husband, if my banishment will bring thee joy, but lay not up this sorrow to thy soul, to reject in folly the gift of God and the flower of all thy line."

But he cried: "The Grecian maid will bear me a fairer son, more worthy to be king of kings. Wherefore should I raise up to majesty the seed of my father's foe?"

"Nay, these are the words of the Greek upon thy tongue, and not thine own."

"Though they be the words of the Greek, the deed is mine. Thou and thy son are banished in shame from Viddin. Begone while yet ye may, or as the Lord God liveth before whom I stand, death shall be your portion."

Then the Lady Nada bowed down in token of submission to her lord, and she took her young son and went forth out of Viddin to her fatherland. And her brother received her with compassion for her plight, and anger against the deed of Mihailo.

And he called the Sabor together and spoke unto them in this wise: "The Bulgar Tsar hath wronged the

Lady Nada, rejecting her son, and he hath bound himself unto the Greek and defied us with boastful words. And even now he gathers an army of heathen Yassi and Tartars to fight beside his own, while Andronicus makes ready his strength in Tsarigrad. A fearsome host will they command, my children, not lightly to be overthrown. What course do ye counsel?"

Then the young Dushan let his voice be heard in the Sabor, and he cried: "What course, my King, save to deal blow for blow and avenge our wrong? Shall we dim the glory of our fathers, cowering before Shishman's son? Our treasure-house is rich as his, our mountains yield gold and silver more than we can bear away. For his Yassi and Tartars we will buy Allemans and soldiers out of Spain, and God will give us the victory because we have not led the infidel against the right-believer."

And the counsel of Dushan, wise beyond his years, was upheld by the Sabor, and the King bought Allemans and soldiers out of Spain, arming them with bright weapons and valorous words. And together with his Serbs, the host numbered fifteen thousand.

And the Bulgar Tsar, commanding a like number, led his forces from Viddin by the south to Makedon, and encamped near Velbuzhd to await the coming of Andronicus, and Stefan lay to the north. Yet Mihailo scorned his adversaries, misprizing their strength, and sent his soldiers to pillage the country roundabout, that they might sate their greed upon its plenty.

But in the Serbian camp the young Dushan spoke thus unto the King and his voyevodas: "My lords, three weary days have we waited like timorous deer in the forest for the hunter's arrow, and Mihailo hath sent his soldiers afield for plunder, and the Greek tarries on his way. Now who hath decreed that we must abide their onslaught? Let us issue forth from our lair, and while their strength is scattered, fall upon our foe to their undoing."

And Stefan made answer: "Thy spirit is too rash, my son. Here we are sheltered behind stout walls of rock, from whose heights we may sow havoc among those below. But leaving our refuge, we oppose our unshielded breasts to the enemy's shafts, courting defeat and death."

"Are their shafts deadlier than ours, my father, or their breasts less mortal, that we should fear them? How shall they prevail against us, since triumph is given not to the shining arms but to the valiant heart, and thy soldiers burn for battle, while the Bulgars dream only of the treasure that shall be their meed at the battle's end. They have set blasphemous foot on our fatherland, my lord, and it were more fitting that Nemanya's sons should lash them forth with scourges than await behind stone walls the hour of their pleasure."

And the chieftain Dragash cried: "My voice is with Dushan. Let us go forth!" And many took up his cry, and the voice of the King was overwhelmed.

And suddenly the Bulgars, scattered over the countryside, and the Tsar within his tent, heard the sound of battle-trumpets and looked to the north and beheld the Serbian banners, borne high above glittering spearheads and crested helmets under the noonday sun. And in hot haste Mihailo sent forth the call to arms, and his warriors sped from far and near to his summons. But more swiftly still did our Serbs bear down upon them, the young Dushan at their head.

Fairest of the Nemanyas was he, towering in beauty above the golden-armored Allemans who guarded him, and to all who looked upon him it was as though an archangel led into battle the hosts of the Blest.

And from a nearby hill Stefan marked the encounter, and saw how the Bulgars, who in confusion had drawn up their ranks, fell away before us, and how the Prince, calling cheer to his comrades, pressed ever toward Mihailo's standard, the while his silver-gleaming arrows sped to right and left, taking each one its toll. Then the blood of the King was stirred with battle-lust so fierce that he might not withhold himself from combat, but galloped into the midst of his warriors who cried him welcome and followed joyously whither he led. And they took many noble Bulgars captive, but wheresoever a Tartar raised his head, there he was smitten down.

So that impious host, having gone forth to make war on a righteous people, was put to rout, and those who escaped the sword were driven into the river Struma, and those who shunned a hero's death yielded themselves to the mercy of their captors.

But Mihailo the Tsar fought valiantly, though so thick were the wounds of his body that he might no longer sit upright in the saddle and clung to the neck of his steed, ever plying his sword. Yet when he saw that Dushan and his Allemans were upon him, he turned and fled, thinking still to preserve himself in life. But to no avail, for God caused his charger to stumble upon a stone and, faint with many hurts, he fell to the ground and all his body was shattered.

And seeing that his enemy lay dead by the hand of the Lord, Dushan lifted up his voice and cried: "Who is like unto Thee, O God, among the mighty? Who is like unto Thee, glorious in holiness, fearful in praises, doing wonders? For I trust not in my bow, neither can my sword save me. But Thou hast saved us from our adversaries, and hast put them to shame that hate us."

And the battle's heat being past, Stefan sat among his voyevodas in the cool of day before Mihailo's tent, and the captive boyars stood hard by, and many proud-necked steeds, laden with arms and the rich spoils of war, passed in endless array to gladden the eyes of the King and embitter his foe, yet they made no out-cry, but behind arrogant lips imprisoned their sorrow.

And in the end there came with measured tread Mihailo's steed, bearing his master's body, and the Bul-gars, till then unwitting of his fate, broke into grievous lamentation and fell prostrate, beating their heads in despair upon the earth. And they cried: "Sweet Tsar! Belovèd lord! Is this the crown of thy glory? Art thou robbed not alone of thy treasure, but of life itself? O thou whom we followed, whither art thou gone before us? If thy soul be near, look down on our desolation and weep for us in our woe."

And Stefan cried: "Thou wert high and hast been brought low. Thou wert a Tsar and now art food for worms. Take warning by Mihailo's end, all ye who would break faith with the Serbs."

Then the Bulgar lords abased themselves at his feet and one spoke for all: "O God-loved King, thine is the joy of this day, and ours the tears. Brothers are we to the dust, our pride an empty wind, our Tsar a name. Yet he was thy kinsman, a monarch and no slave, a mighty ruler over mighty men. Be merciful, we pray thee, as thou art blest, and give him burial as beseems a prince."

And Stefan answered: "He shall have burial and ye your freedom, if ye will take the Lady Nada's son to be your lord."

"How shall he be our lord who is yet a child?"

"Let his mother rule in his stead till his years be ripe. And if ye will not, I will hang you from yonder tree and seize your domains and the land of the Bulgars shall be subject to the Serb."

And they cried: "Let Nada's son be Tsar," and by the body and blood of Christ they swore to yield him homage.

Then the King commanded that the bones of Mihailo be laid to rest with song and prayer in the church of

Kumanovo, and to all the Christian dead he gave burial, but the heathen he left to be devoured by vultures.

And the hosts of Andronicus, learning of what was befallen, turned their backs upon us and fled, and our troops pursued them, driving them beyond our borders. And when they had cleansed the land of all invaders, they returned in triumph to white Skoplie. And bells pealed from the towers and beaconfires burned on the high hills to welcome them.

And the people made merry in the streets and the King in his castle, and they drank red wine while the guslars sang of the mighty deeds of Stefan and his son Dushan. And at length the King rose up from his place and cried: "By the grace of the Lord and the prayers of Saint Simeon and Saint Sava, we have prevailed over our adversaries. And ye have sung our praises, but the praises of Him who upheld us in His hands ye have not sung. Let us sing them, my children, not with the pipe and the gusle, nor with the lifting up of voices alone, but with songs more enduring. In the cave of Yovan, there where the All-Merciful restored the sight to mine eyes, our father Sava appeared to me in a vision and said: 'In thine earthly majesty shalt thou come hither again and do honor to Him who is the Lord of lords and the King of kings.' Now shall his word be made truth, for I would build in that place a shrine of white silver and burning gold,

103

adorned with pearls and many-colored jewels, and covered with a roof of lead. And it shall be called High Detchanye and, brighter than sunlight, it shall stand forever, bearing witness to our love of God and His service to us on the battlefield of Velbuzhd."

And his nobles and bishops raised high their chalices and cried: "Build, Stefan! Build to the glory of God and the triumph of Velbuzhd!"

Then the Lady Nada bowed before her brother and, kissing his hand, she cried: "My lord, this battle was fought for me. And on the morrow I go forth from my father's land to the land of my son, where I am not loved, and who knows what the end may be? Wherefore, I pray thee, let me speak my meaning ere I depart."

And Stefan said: "Speak, my sister."

"Build not this shrine of gold and silver and precious stones, my King, for in the ancient books it hath been prophesied that our land shall fall a prey to heathen. And they will tear down the church of the true God, and melt thy gold and silver, and fill their coffers with thy precious jewels, and the Lord, looking down from heaven, will shed bitter tears to see His altar despoiled. But if thou wilt send thy master builder beyond the Grecian seas, he will find there a stone brighter than gold and more precious than pearls, that fire may not burn nor the power of man destroy. Let him bear away in ships so much as will serve thy need, and build High Detchanye in the valley of the Bistritsa to stand till the horns shall sound God's Judgment Day."

And Stefan cried: "Praise be thine, sweet Nada,

praise for thy counsel and the wisdom of thy words."
And he bade his master builder sail beyond the Grecian seas and bear away the stone brighter than gold
and more precious than pearls whereof his sister had
told. And he built High Detchanye in the green valley that lies beneath the cave of Yovan, so high that
the eye wearies to look upon it, so fair that it outshines
the golden sun. And from that time forth, Stefan was
named Detchanski for the wonder he had wrought,
that stands to this day since fire may not burn nor the
power of man destroy it.

OW let the sun and stars and all that lives by their light bear witness how evil demons lurk within man's breast, goading him to his doom. For surely none was more favored of God than Stefan, having begot a hero unto his fathers and an heir to his line greater than all who had gone before him. Yet because his people honored the young Dushan, crying: "Hail, falcon of Velbuzhd! Long life to the Nemanyitch!" the King, who should have rejoiced, was moved to envy. And he looked coldly upon his son, and to those who were in his counsels let fall the word that Symeon should be his heir.

But his princes opposed themselves to his will, crying: "By the marriage bed to which we led thee, thou didst make oath that the issue of Mara's womb should not be king. Wilt thou play us false, bidding us bow the head before a Greek?"

And Stefan, lashed by his evil demons to fury, answered: "I am your master and ye shall not command me nor forbid me in aught. The oath I made by my marriage bed I now renounce, and by my life and yours I swear to you that Symeon shall be king."

And in token of his purpose, he led his troops to the west and laid in ruins the castle of Dushan. And the young King grieved, nor would he lift up his hand against Stefan, for dearer to him than castles or glory was his father's love. And he cried: "Since I am become hateful in his sight, I will betake myself where his eyes shall not look upon me, nor his ears hear the sound of my name."

But his nobles and councilors, they who had forsaken Stefan, said unto him: "Betray not the trust of thy fathers, Nemanya's son, nor deliver up thy people to a Grecian lord. The King is possessed of a fiend, and knows not his heart. Be thou the King till he hath been made whole, and for thy love he will bless thee in after days."

And Dushan was moved by their words to lead them against his father, whom he defeated, and Stefan was brought captive before him. And he cried: "In my youth I lay enchained at my father's feet; in mine age, at thine. Would God I had not lived to endure this day!"

And Dushan answered: "Thou shalt be kindly kept till the fiend that possesses thy soul be driven forth. And when thou art whole again, we will rule together once more in peace and friendship."

But the enemies of Stefan cast him into the dungeons at Zvechan, and the Nemanyitch was anointed King.

And when the hapless Stefan had languished for two full moons in his dungeon, there entered in to him by

Arna-uts, rent by Grecian strife, fall under his sway, and ere long he ruled from the Danube to the walls of Tsarigrad and from Pomorye to the shores of the Black Sea. And over all the world his name echoed like the sound of clamorous bells, and envoys came from the courts of the mighty to bend the knee before him, and the free city of Venice inscribed him in her Golden Book, together with Yelena the Queen, and the young Prince Urosh.

Now when God's purpose in these things was made manifest unto Dushan, he faltered not but followed boldly his high destiny, and appearing before the Sabor, he cried: "Kings were my fathers who ruled over the Serbian land and over Pomorye. But I, their son, rule over many kingdoms that my fathers knew not, and many whom they served now pay me tribute. And I have done what none before me might do, despoiling the Greek, till all his jewels save Tsarigrad alone shine in my crown. Yet still this crown that adorns my brow is the crown of a king, though kings are my vassals and no tsar is my peer. I pray you, my people, look upon my deeds and judge me, if I am not worthy to be named your king of kings!"

And they cried: "Hail, king of kings! Long years to Tsar Dushan!"

And so it came to pass that on the Day of the Lord's Resurrection, there gathered in the church of Skoplie all our high nobles and godly bishops, yea, and princes

from far lands, clad in pearls and cloth of purple and shining gold to make glad the eye. And the monks of the Holy Mountain came to honor him who had poured treasure like grain into their coffers, and the king knelt before Yovanniki, he who had been Archbishop in Serbia and now was named Patriarch, since the Tsar may not be crowned save by the hand of a Father in the church. And Yovanniki placed on the head of Dushan a golden crown, fairer than the crown of Tsarigrad, and he cried: "By the will of God, made manifest unto me, and with his solemn blessing, I crown thee, Stefan Dushan, Tsar of the Serbs, the Bulgars and the Greeks!" And with joyful hearts and voices the people acclaimed him, crying: "God and the Tsar! Live forever, thou who hast shed light and glory upon us!"

Then the Tsar arose from his knees, and with a lesser crown he crowned Yelena his Tsaritsa, and with the crown of a king he crowned his son. And kissing the hand that had exalted them, they took place beside him, while the holy men of Athos sang praise to God for that He had guided our Saviour from the tomb to the realms of eternal life, and had granted our king that he should be crowned a tsar.

Now many noble lords sought favor at the court of Tsar Dushan, and he honored them, but three there were whom he loved beyond their brethren, and one was Pribatz, his counselor, father of Lazar, and one was Branko, who begot the traitor Vuk, and the third was the wily Vukashin, who requited the love of the Tsar by such foul deeds as ye shall weep to hear. And he gave them fair provinces to rule as their own, and the fairest he gave unto Vukashin, white Skadar by Boyana's stream.

HE light that flashes from the summer sky, on the edge of a sword, in a woman's eyes, beware, my son! Fearful are they and fraught with dire peril, and the last is most perilous. For high above thy head the lightning plays, and from the sword thou canst defend thyself, but a woman's eyes that would lure thee to the Pit, may smile upon thee like the gates of Paradise. The light that flashes from the summer sky, on the edge of a sword, in a woman's eyes, beware, my son! For they are three bright roads leading to death, and the last is the surest.

In the mountains of Pirlitor, like a king in his tower, dwelt Momchilo the Outlaw, whose fame was spread abroad through all the wide Serbian land for his deeds of daring, and his followers faithful and bold, and his wingèd steed. Yet the fame of these things was as naught to the fame of Vidosava, his wife. For it was told that in the four corners of the earth there was none to match her, neither among the Grecians nor the

113

slender Vlachs nor the white maidens of Venice. And those who had seen the Veela of the mountains swore that the Veela must hide her face in shame before the beauty of Vidosava.

Now Vukashin, holding the fortress of Skadar by the will of the great Dushan, sent secretly to the Lady Vidosava his messenger. And he said: "Thou wife of Momchilo, to whose beauty all men pay homage, say, art thou content to dwell forever amid the snows of mournful Pirlitor? What dost thou see, gazing aloft from thy casement, under the summer as the winter sun? Naught save the icy peaks of Durmitor. What dost thou see below save the gloomy Tara, bearing huge boulders and the stumps of trees on her wild journey to the sea? And all thy castle is ringed about with rocks and bleak pine woods, nor canst thou cross the Tara by any bridge nor scale high Durmitor. Wherefore do thou poison thy husband Momchilo, or betray him into my hands, and when he is destroyed, thou shalt come with me to Skadar on Boyana's stream, to be my lady. Silk shalt thou spin upon a golden spindle, and thy raiment shall be fashioned of rich fabrics from the looms of Venice, and a crown of gold shalt thou wear to crown thy beauty. Fair is Skadar that rises on Boyana's banks. Gazing aloft, thou shalt look upon sunny hillsides, teeming with figs and olives and the purple grapevine; and below thou shalt see broad wheatfields and flowering meadows watered by the green Boyana, where many fishes swim, and when it is thy fancy, thou shalt eat of them, new netted from the stream."

114

And when the fair Vidosava had read the message of Vukashin, she sent him this word in reply: "O thou my lord Vukashin! No simple task hast thou set me, bidding me either poison my husband Momchilo or betray him into thy hands. For thou must know that Momchilo hath nine brothers and twelve brothers' sons and a sister Yevrosima. And Yevrosima makes ready the food that he eats and tastes of each dish before him, and his brothers serve him with rakia and with wine and drink of each cup before him. And behind his chair stand the twelve sons of his brothers to guard him from attack. Moreover, he hath a wingèd steed, Yabuchilo, to bear him whither he will, and a sword with eyes. Yet by a woman's wit and the might of a prince a man may be overthrown. Each sevenight on the Holy Day of the Lord, Momchilo is wont to ride into the forest to hunt wild deer, and with him ride his brothers and the sons of his brothers and all his train. Do thou assemble a goodly company, and lie in wait for them behind the thicket that borders the woodland pool, and for my part, I will contrive that the wings of Yabuchilo shall be burned, and the eyes of the sword sealed fast with salt red blood. If thou slay Momchilo, I will go with thee to Skadar to be thy lady, but take heed that he slay not thee."

Then, having received the message of Vidosava, Vukashin assembled a goodly company, and led them into high Hercegovina where Durmitor climbs to the skies, and they came to the woodland pool in the midst of the forest on the eve of the Holy Day.

Now Lord Momchilo had lain him down betimes

115

upon his pallet against the morrow's chase, and awaited the coming of Vidosava. But when she entered in to him, the tears fell like bright pearls from her eyes, nor were they less radiant to behold than those that were bound in the raven plaits of her hair.

And Momchilo cried: "What grief is thine, my wife, that thy tears flow down? And though they rather adorn than dim thy beauty, yet I would not see thee weep. Come, lie beside me that I may comfort thee."

But Vidosava would not, and when he rose and strove to stem her tears, she turned from him and wept the more.

And at length he cried: "If thou wilt but say to me, my swan, my fair one, wherefore thou dost weep and what is needful to thy happiness, before the dawn thou shalt hold it in thy hands, though it be the crown of Tsarigrad."

And she answered: "No crown do I crave but the crown of thy trust, Lord Momchilo. Full often have I heard it said that Yabuchilo thy steed is a wingèd steed, yet have I never beheld his wings, and when I have sued for this boon, thou hast answered me, 'No woman may behold them.' Yet now it is come to mine ears that Yevrosima, thy sister, each evening visits his stall and anoints his plumage with sweet-smelling oils, with balsam and with myrrh. Is Yevrosima no woman? Or doth she belike go blindfold to the task? Nay, it is I, thy wife, that lives unhonored in thy castle and the mock of thy lowest thrall."

And Momchilo laughed aloud from his full throat, for though he was ripe in wisdom, she had beguiled

116

him. And clasping her to his breast, he cried: "If this be all thy plaint, belovèd wife, go with the first cock's crow to Yabuchilo's stall, when he doth spread his wings in all their glory, and gaze thy fill."

So saying, he led her to his pallet and she lay beside him, and presently he slumbered. But Vidosava slumbered not, awaiting the first cock's crow, and when it smote upon her ears, she rose from the pallet and lighted a waxen taper, and with tar and tallow went forth to the stall of Yabuchilo.

Ah, that ye might have beheld the wonder of Yabuchilo's wings, spread high to the beams of his stall and low to his hoofs, for it was the wonder of clouds that sail through the sky and of birds in flight. But Vidosava, may her soul be curst, anointed them with tallow and with tar, and kindled them at the flame of her waxen taper and burned them to ashes, and what she might not utterly destroy she bound fast to his knees. Then she hied her to the arsenal of her lord, and with the salt blood of a lamb new slain sealed fast the eyes of his sword that they might not see his peril. And having wrought this evil against him, she returned to his couch and lay down beside him and slept.

And when the dawn broke white above Durmitor, Momchilo awoke and spoke to Vidosava, saying: "Strange is the dream that troubled my rest this night, for I dreamed that out of the cursèd land of Vasoye, a wreath of mist curled like a serpent over Durmitor, and through the mist I rode with my brothers and the sons of my brothers and all my train. And ever its folds pressed thicker and darker upon me, swallowing my

117

comrades, and though I turned my steed hither and yon, and called on their names that the hills clamored to hear me, I found them no more. Surely this is a dream that bodes no good, and I will not hunt today."

And she answered: "A brave dream for a brave knight, my lord. And what dost thou fear, since dreams are lies and God alone is the truth?"

Then Momchilo knew shame of his fears and arrayed himself for the chase, and Vidosava led forth his steed from the stall, and from the arsenal brought his seeing sword and girded it upon him, and amidst his brethren and the sons of his brethren and the faithful ones of his train, Momchilo rode to the chase.

But when they were come to the pool in the heart of the forest, from behind the thicket Vukashin burst upon them at the head of his troops, and swiftly surrounded them. And Momchilo drew his sword from out of its sheath, crying in anger: "O thou my seeing sword, wherefore didst thou not warn me of the peril awaiting us?"

But the sword answered: "Mine eyes are blind, sealed by thy wife with the blood of a lamb new slain."

Then Momchilo rallied his kinsmen and comrades about him, and cried in the voice of a lion: "Hear ye, my brethren! Vidosava, may the Lord burn her soul in everlasting fire, hath betrayed us! Yet though we be outnumbered, let each man fight with the fury of a hundred and our strength will outweigh the foe's. Now do ye fall upon their flanks and hew them down, and I will charge into their midst."

And as he said, so did they. Like a falcon among

doves did Momchilo strike into the midst of his foe! To the left and the right he scattered them, and as many as he slew by the sword, nay, more, did Yabuchilo trample beneath his hoofs, and their bodies were a path whereon his master pressed forward toward Pirlitor. Yet where good fortune is, ill fortune follows, for Momchilo beheld in the field nine plunging steeds, yea, the nine black steeds of his brothers did he behold, and they were riderless. Then the heart of the hero broke for his born brethren, and the sword fell from his hand, and leaning low on the neck of Yabuchilo, he whispered to his steed: "Fly swiftly, my Chilas, to the castle, for only thy wings lie between us and death!" But Yabuchilo answered not nor flew.

Then Momchilo cried: "In a black night wert thou foaled, may wolves devour thee! How often have we flown together, spurning the earth for very gladness of heart, though no need drove us. Yet now, with the foe at our heels and death before us, thou wilt not fly!"

And Yabuchilo answered: "May thy curse light on her head that hath earned it, Momchilo! I do not fly because I cannot fly. Thy Vidosava hath burned my wings to ashes, and what she might not utterly destroy she hath bound fast to my knees. Wherefore do thou flee as thou canst, dear master, for my service to thee is at an end."

Now the hot hears flowed from the eyes of Momchilo in pity for his steed, yet hotter was the wrath that blazed like living flame in his breast against the false Vidosava. And his limbs were become as oaks

119

and his heart as a mountain, and he leaped from the back of Yabuchilo and in three bounds had reached the castle gate. But the gate was bolted and sealed, and though he beat upon it with blows of iron, none came to open and he might not enter in.

Then he cried: "Dear sister Yevrosima, fling me a length of linen from thy casement, that I may mount to thy chamber and escape mine enemies!"

And her voice answered: "Alas, my brother, how shall I fling thee linen or come in any wise to thine aid, since Vidosava thy wife hath bound me by my hair unto a beam!"

Thus did she make reply to her brother, but her deeds overleaped her words, for when she heard from afar the shouts of the foe, new strength flowed into her limbs, and with such fury did she swing her head, hissing the while as an angry serpent hisses, that her hair was torn from its roots, setting her free. And in that moment when Vukashin raised his sword to smite her brother's head from his shoulders, she flung from her casement a length of linen truly woven, and Momchilo seized it, and drew himself aloft, out of the reach of the blade of his enemy.

And now he mounts swiftly to his sister's chamber, and leaning from her place, she reaches her white hand to his aid, but alas, for her loyal heart and the love that would have saved him! Ere he can grasp her hand, his faithless wife steals from behind her and with a keen-edged dagger severs the rope above her husband's head. So Momchilo fell, the mighty hero fell upon the sabers of Vukashin's men, on their sabers and spears, on their axes and battle-maces did he fall, and his life poured forth from his body by a hundred wounds. And they laid him at the feet of Vukashin who plunged his sword through his enemy's living heart. Yet still he would not die, may his deeds live forever on the tongues of his countrymen, but holding his heart between his hands, he spoke: "Take not my false Vidosava into thy bed, Vukashin, for as she hath betrayed me to thee this day, so will she betray thee on the morrow to another. But take in her stead my sister Yevrosima. Faithful is Yevrosima unto death, and will bear thee a son in the image of her brother, yet mightier still than Momchilo—a hero whose like hath not been known in Serbia nor will not be again."

So saying, Momchilo yielded up his spirit, and his body perished. And Vukashin commanded that it be borne on a litter through the streets of Pirlitor, that the people might know that he who had been their lord was their lord no more.

Then Vidosava came forth out of the castle, and her maidens upheld her flowing sleeves and the hem of her robe. And she bowed low before Vukashin, then laid her white hand in his and drew him within. And at the golden sofra she served him with white loaves and the flesh of rams, with rakia and red wine. And when he had eaten, she caused raiment to be spread before him that had been her lord's, and his weapons and his armor. And lo! dear God! a marvel! For the tunic that had fallen to the knees of Momchilo fell to Vukashin's feet, and the helmet that had clasped the head of Momchilo lay on Vukashin's shoulders. And the fair gold ring wherewith he had been wont to deck his finger girdled three fingers of Vukashin's hand, and the boot wherein he had thrust his good right leg held both legs of his foe. And when Vukashin strove to grasp the sword that Momchilo had borne in battle, he might not raise it but sank beneath its burden to the ground.

And the words of Momchilo rang in Vukashin's ears, blighting the woman's beauty, and he thought: "Wise was his counsel, and I were a fool to scorn it. For she that would betray so matchless a hero, whose like the world hath not known, how should she keep faith with Vukashin when another comes, whose lands are broader than mine and his treasure richer?"

And turning his eyes from the face of Vidosava, he cried: "Ho! Ye that serve me! Take this woman and bind her to the tails of three wild steeds and let them tear asunder her white body that shall nevermore entice the hearts of men!"

And so it was done. But Vukashin took the meek Yevrosima to be his wife, and she bare him two sons, and one was named with the name of Andreash, and one with the name of Marko. And Andreash was a goodly youth, well-favored and bold of spirit, but Marko was made in the image of Momchilo, yet mightier still than he, a hero whose like hath not been known in Serbia nor will not be again. And for many long years Vukashin abode in Skadar, but Marko he sent to be bred at the court of Dushan and to be his scribe.

122

MONG the Turks a tale is told of Osman, their father, and they tell it in this wise.

Being overtaken by darkness on the road to Brusa, Osman found shelter beneath the roof of a learned man, who gave him food for his hunger and a pallet for his sweet repose. And parting from his guest, he laid into his hand a Book as though he laid a jewel, saying: "Allah send rest to thy body and thy weary soul."

And Osman cried: "What book is this that like a precious gift thou hast laid into my hand?"

And he answered: "The word of Allah, by the mouth of Mohammed, His Prophet."

And wondering, Osman opened the Book and read, and its pages were fraught with wisdom that bathed his spirit as in the waters of a mountain lake. And so rapt was he that he might not put the Book from out his hand, but stood and read till the dawn, then sank upon his pallet in heavy slumber. And an angel of the Lord Allah appeared unto him, saying: "Because thou hast read with love the word of my Master,

123

thy children and thy children's children shall be honored from generation to generation."

And the angel vanished, and Osman dreamed that he lay beside the father of his wife, out of whose loins a crescent moon arose and waxed to fullness. And being full, the moon descended into the loins of Osman, whence presently a tree sprang forth, and budded and bore fruit, spreading its branches ever more thickly above him till its shadow embraced the earth. And beneath the tree great mountains reared their heads, and among its roots wide rivers flowed, covered with ships like the sea. And the fields were ripe with harvests, and forests decked the mountain slopes, and all the green valleys held golden-domed cities, from whose towers sounded the call to prayer.

Then the leaves of the mighty tree that sprang from his loins were transformed to sword-blades, and a wind moved among them, pointing them toward Tsarigrad. And he turned and beheld that city of desire, lying where two seas meet and two bodies of land, like a stone of white between stones of blue and green. And to Osman they were as the jewels of a vast ring that encircled the world. And putting forth his hand, he took the ring and drew it upon his finger, and awoke.

Now whether this tale be true or false, my children, I know not, knowing only that all it presaged is come to pass through the wickedness of the Tsar Kantakuzen. For the infidel had been content to tarry within the bounds appointed him of God, but the Tsar, envious

124

of our blessings, bought him for gold, and led him in countless hordes across the sea to give us battle, his Grecians being scant and poor-spirited. And he gave them arms and taught them the ways of our warfare and, sin of sins! bestowed in marriage upon Orchan, Osman's son, the hand of his right-believing daughter.

So the Turk, who with wrath and curses should have been beaten back, was welcomed in friendship, and he looked long upon our wooded mountains and our wide rivers, covered with ships like the sea, and our richly-blooming fields, and a flame was lighted within him of desire and lust, that grew to a mighty blaze, consuming all our land in its holocaust, and leaving behind a desert and darkness and tears.

But the great Dushan, God have pity on his blighted years, saw clearly the shadow that lay upon us, and he said: "I will take Tsarigrad from this godless monarch who befouls the banner of Christ, and I will thrust him from his throne into the mire, together with his heathen son." And he summoned Vukashin from Skadar, and from Ochrid his voyevoda Branko, and marched at the head of his glorious host to the south. And Lazar, son of Pribatz, was his standard-bearer, and Marko, son of Vukashin, was his scribe.

Yet sorrow and not joy was our destiny, for the leech of Dushan was a Greek, skilled beyond all his kind in the art of healing, and a faithful servant until that day when his master resolved to assail the city of his

125

forebears. Then bitterness galled his blood, and from friend he was transformed into ruthless foe.

Now our Tsar, hale as a tree that the sun and rains have nourished for many a year, feasted within his tent, unwitting of peril. And he cried: "Sing, Marko! Set free thy voice that outroars the thunderbolt! Sing, Marko, in praise of the red wine that cools our throats and warms our deepest bowels."

And Marko sang: "At the foot of a hill, below fruitful vineyards, dwelt an ancient man whose heart was merry. And all his joy was to sit, beaker in hand, among his comrades, drinking draught for draught, and gladdening with his laughter the quiet hills. For thou must know, my Tsar, that in all the world no laughter rang so blithe as his. And first and last, raising his beaker, he cried: 'My Father in the sky, with rosy wine and a contented soul I drink to Thee.'

"Then sounded the dread Horn of the Judgment Day, and the souls of all men stood in shining garments before the Lord God, high on His golden throne. Yet, looking among them, He found not whom He sought and cried to Saint Peter: 'Bring hither yonder graybeard who trembles behind the gates of pearl, thinking to escape my wrath.'

"And rudely Saint Peter seized him, and drew him before the Lord God, crying: 'Let him burn in hellfire, Father, for the fiends have kindled a merry blaze to receive him. No service hath he rendered Thee on earth, but all his joy was to sit, beaker in hand, among his comrades, quaffing red wine, and troubling with his laughter the quiet hills. Let him drain a cup of

126

brimstone, Lord, for each cup of honeyed wine he drained on earth.'

"But the Lord God smiled on the ancient sinner kneeling humbly at his feet, and said unto him: 'Well hast thou known how to savor my gifts to man of wine and laughter and kind fellowship, and for thine open heart, my son, I love thee. But he who frowns and turns aside his head from these my blessings is the thief, and not the lord, of life. Wherefore I bid thee enter into Paradise, and praise Me in the wine of heaven as on earth thou didst praise Me.'

"And the graybeard entered into Paradise and seized with both hands the blessèd chalice proffered by fair cherubim, and lifting it high, he cried: 'My Father in the sky, with rosy wine and a contented soul I drink to Thee.'"

And Dushan, being well pleased with the song of Marko, cried: "Wine! Bring rosy wine that we may drink to our Father in the sky!"

And his cupbearer proffered unto the Tsar the accursèd chalice, poisoned by the hand of his leech, and rising from his place, he cried: "Lords and not thieves of life are we, dear God, loving wine and laughter and kind fellowship. Do Thou smile upon us as upon that ancient dweller among vineyards!"

And his nobles cried: "Do thou smile upon us, Lord God!" and drained their cups, whose wine like a river of joy flowed through their limbs. But the Tsar's black draught robbed his eyes of light, and his heart of laughter, and the chalice fell from his hand, and he gazed

127

upon those gathered in terror about him as one who gazes from a far country.

But Dushan the Mighty yielded not up his soul to death till he had made known his will unto Marko, his scribe. And this was the will of Dushan: "Since Urosh, my son, is yet of tender age and unskilled in ruling, let my faithful servant, the wise Lord Vukashin, hold in trust for seven years all the fair lands won by Nemanya's sword. And for seven years, let him hold sway over my people and fulfill my laws upon them, but when the eighth year dawns, he shall deliver up his trust unto Urosh, my rightful heir. And for this service he shall be called king in Prilep, but Urosh shall be anointed Tsar."

And Marko wrote down his words from the lips of Dushan, sealing them with his seal, that none might gainsay them. And the Protopope Nedyelko washed him clean of sin, and having made his peace with earth and heaven, he closed his eyes from this world.

ITTER was his end to us but sweet to his foe. For the hosts he had led to Tsarigrad returned to Prizren, bearing his body in their midst, and when with their tears they had laid him beneath the dome of the Archangel Mihailo, there was none to lead them forth again. For the wily Vukashin, smiling the smile of a serpent in his beard, spoke unto the Sabor, saying: "In God's good time we will take Tsarigrad, crowning the labors of Dushan. But let us first build anew the walls of our cities lest they fall into alien hands and, striving for fresh conquests, we lose what is already won."

And the Sabor praised his wisdom, knowing not his secret thought. But, alas for us! we know, my children, that neither against the Turk nor the Magyar did Vukashin seek to defend our strongholds, but against Urosh, their rightful lord, and those who, out of love for the dead Tsar, named themselves friends to Urosh. And as he had decreed, it was brought to pass, the walls of all our cities being builded anew, higher and stronger than of old. And himself, he journeyed to

129

Skadar on Boyana's river, for there he thought to build himself a fortress that should be the fortress of a tsar.

With Vukashin to Skadar went all his household save Marko Kralyevitch, whom he left behind to rule in white Prilep; and with him went his brothers, the Despot Uglesha and Goyko the Brave; and with him went Rado, his master builder, and three hundred of his men.

And when they were come to Skadar, and the tents had been pitched, and the fortress of Dushan razed to the very ground, Rado commanded his men to lay the foundation for the walls of the new fortress, that should stand staunch against the four winds of heaven and the onslaughts of mighty armies, to the everlasting glory of King Vukashin and the confusion of his enemy.

And with stout hearts and arms all day they plied their task, and at setting of the sun the foundation was firmly laid. But when they came with the dawn to labor again, lo! all they had done was undone, and the stones that had lain sweetly cheek by cheek were crushed and broken, and where they had left the roots of a mighty fortress, they found a shattered pit.

But Rado, who was a man of wisdom nor spent his strength in lamentation, cried: "It is some enemy of the King that hath wrought this mischief and on his trespass let the King pass judgment. But as for us, we will lay the foundation anew."

And with such good will did they labor on this, the second day of their building that, ere the setting sun, the foundation was laid anew and one fair wall rose to the mountain's height. And Rado set a guard of threescore men to keep watch over the fortress, and they kept watch through the night. But when the morning star had bathed her face and risen to look out upon the world, she saw them lying in enchanted slumber, and all about them lay Skadar in ruins.

And Rado came and beheld the destruction of his handiwork, and would have fallen upon his slumbering guard to slay them. Yet even as he raised his arm to smite, he saw that theirs was no simple slumber but the fruit of some evil charm. And he stayed his hand and strove to rouse them but might not, nor might their comrades, till the golden sunlight, scattering the darkness, unclosed their eyes. Then Rado questioned them, but how the enchantment had been laid upon them or by whom, they knew not.

Whereupon he cried: "Yet once again will we plant this fortress, my children, and send it springing toward heaven. And tonight I, Rado, will watch beside it, and if they be mortal hands that tear it down, I will tear them from the arms where they grow. But if this be the work of a Veela, we will build no more."

And so they builded on the third day, and so strong were their hearts in the strength of their master's word that, ere the setting sun, two mighty walls shadowed the plain, bearing witness to the power of Rado and his men over all other builders. And Rado looked upon his labor and found it good, and when night

131

came, he stood alone beneath the sky to watch beside it.

Now when the night was darkest, the lovely Veela of the mountains descended and would have laid her hands upon the eyes of Rado, but he flung her from him, crying: "Work thy mischief before my seeing eyes, for Rado will not heed thy spell."

And a peal of mocking laughter smote his ears, then swift and silent as an evil dream his two proud walls crumbled and sank to earth, and of all that the day had wrought the night left no sign nor hope.

Wherefore Rado took his weary way at dawn to the tent of Vukashin, and related to him all that was come to pass, and that day no stone was laid for the building of the fortress of Skadar. But when the night was darkest, King Vukashin stood at the foot of the Veela's mountain and cried unto her: "Ho! Veela! What is my sin against thee that thou dost hinder the building of my citadel Skadar?"

And she answered: "Sins hast thou sinned in full measure, King Vukashin, but none against me. Yet it pleases me to hinder the building of thy citadel Skadar, and now I tell thee that though thy builders labor for thrice three hundred days and thou spill thy treasure like sand, treasure and labor alike will be spilled in vain, for what they rear by day, by night I will overthrow."

"And will naught move thee, Veela, from thy purpose?"

"Now hearken to me well, wily Vukashin. One road there is that will lead thee to thy goal and I will

132

show it thee. But 'tis a road unblessed, that rises in grief and ends in blood and death. Wilt thou take it, King?"

"I will take it, Veela."

"Then hear me. Ye are three brothers, wed each to a faithful wife. Let her among your wives who on the morrow bears their midday meal to the builders be seized by them and buried deep in the wall's foundations. Only thus shall ye fix them firmly; only thus shall ye build your vaunted fortress on Boyana's banks."

And laden with her heavy words, Vukashin hied him homeward, and summoned his brothers, and told them all the tale of his encounter with the Veela. And when he had done, he said: "Now let us swear, my brothers, in God's holy presence and by our brotherhood, to reveal naught of the dread knowledge that hath been vouchsafed us, but do the Veela's will upon her whom fate shall lead on the morrow to bear their midday meal to the builders. And the grief of one shall be the grief of all."

And with their hands clasped one upon the other, the brothers swore the oath in God's holy presence, and having sworn, returned each one to his dwelling, where his wife abided his coming.

And an ill thing was done, for Vukashin did violence to the oath he had sworn, breaking faith with his brothers in these words to the meek Yevrosima: "Go not abroad on the morrow, neither to bear their midday meal to the builders, nor for any purpose soever. Seek not to know my reasons, but do my bidding."

133

And Uglesha did violence to the oath he had sworn, breaking faith with his brothers in these words to the proud Eufemia: "Bear not on the morrow their midday meal to the builders, lest evil overtake thee and thou perish in the fragrance of thy youth."

But Goyko the Brave kept faith with his faithless brothers, and lying beside his bride with an anguished heart, yet spoke no word in her ear. And on the morrow he bade farewell to the gentle Rosanda and bade farewell to the suckling babe at her breast, and fared him forth to the green banks of the Boyana, there to await what destiny should decree.

And as the sun grew in splendor, the Queen Yevrosima dispatched a messenger to the wife of Uglesha with these words: "The King hath forbade my going abroad this day, either to bear their midday meal to the builders or for any purpose soever. Do thou, therefore, sister-in-God, go with the serving maidens to the Boyana, and on the morrow I will take thy place."

But Eufemia lifted high her voice in laughter and cried: "Queen art thou, yet I am not thy fool!" And she went to Goyko's dwelling, where Rosanda sang beside her golden loom while her mother rocked the babe in his cradle.

And she said: "Sister, my head is heavy and I fear the burning light of the sun. Do thou go forth today with the serving maidens, and bear to the builders their midday meal."

And Rosanda answered: "Gladly would I go, but my babe is wakeful and my stint at the loom is not yet done."

"I will finish thy stint, and sing to thy babe till he fall into quiet slumber."

And straightway Rosanda arose from her place, though her mother would have stayed her, saying: "Go not, my daughter, for indeed it is not needful, but let the serving maidens for this day bear the meal to the Boyana unattended."

"Nay, mother, men will cry us shame if, out of three, not one is ready to attend the maidens for our husbands' pleasure."

Swiftly then she summoned the serving maidens, and went in their midst toward the green banks of the Boyana. And from afar young Goyko knew her by her quiet gait, as of a lamb that follows his mother to pleasant pastures. And his heart froze within him and when she drew nigh, she saw that all was not well with him, and laying her white hand upon his arm, she said: "What is amiss, my lord, that thine eyes stare and the dew is moist on thy brow?"

And he answered: "Evil, dear love. The golden dagger that was thy gift to me hath fallen into Boyana's waters and vanished."

And laughing, she replied: "Pray earnestly to the Lord, my husband, and it may be He will send thee a fairer dagger."

But young Goyko turned aside for the red wound that bled in his heart, and Vukashin took her white hand in his and called upon Rado, saying: "Do what thou hast to do."

And Rado called upon his builders, saying: "Do what ye have to do."

And Rosanda stood laughing in their midst as they heaped the rock and the heavy beams about her, for she deemed their work the sport of an idle hour. And now she is enclosed to the knees, but still she smiles upon them, crying: "Enough, good friends. Eat with God's blessing the viands I have brought you, and let me go to feed my babe at home."

But they speak no word in answer, piling the heavy beams and rock about her till they have reached her girdle. And her smile gives place to doubt and her doubt to terror, and a shriek like the shriek of a wild gull wounded in flight, rings to the sea. And now she stretches fearful hands to her brothers, crying: "As God looks down on you, have mercy with me! Have mercy, mighty King! Mercy, Uglesha! Can ye destroy me, slender and green as I am, a young birch-tree in the forest?"

But her brothers turned aside their heads, giving no heed to her prayer.

And now in her anguish she calls upon Goyko, her husband, he by whose side she has lain, her bridegroom, her lover: "Wilt thou suffer them to do me harm, my lord? Wherein have I offended, wherein failed thee? Faithful to my troth have I been, in body and soul— yea, even now as thou dost stand apart, watching thy brothers work their will upon me, my heart cries out to thee in love."

And Goyko drew nigh, and took her white face in his hands and kissed her sweet lips: "O my wife, dear sorrow of my heart! Didst thou never dream that thou must perish? Was there no wind to whisper in

136

thine ear: 'Bide at home with thy babe! Go not forth to thy doom, Rosanda!' In vain dost thou sue to me, in vain to my brothers. It is the will of the Veela they wreak upon thee by an oath of brotherhood."

Then young Goyko turned him to where Vukashin the King and the Despot Uglesha stood side by side, and he spoke to them in this wise: "As ye have dealt falsehood or truth unto me this day, my brothers, so may it be dealt unto you in the hour of your death. But as for me, I shall stand by your side no more." And drawing his sword from its sheath, he broke it in twain, and turned and vanished into the forest, nevermore to be seen of men.

And Rosanda, seeing that her prayers were of no avail, ceased from lamentation and turned her face to Rado, the master builder.

And she said: "I pray thee, master Rado, in God's name, my little Yovo hath lived scarce a moon, and though it be the Veela's will that I die, why must he perish too? Enclose me in the tower if thou wilt, but leave two windows, one for my white breast, that Yovo may drink life therefrom, one for mine eyes that they may behold him as he is borne hither and as he is borne homeward again."

And Rado heeded her plea as a brother might. High they builded the wall of stone about her but left two windows, one for her snowy breast that her babe might drink life therefrom, one for her eyes that they might behold him as he was borne thither and as he was borne homeward again. High they builded the wall of stone about her, and day by day, at dawn, at noon-

137

tide and at setting sun, they brought him to her that she might suckle him. And for seven days her voice was heard, murmuring words of love and sorrow, but on the eighth day it ceased, and was heard no more.

Yet still the stream of life flowed from her breast to feed the nursling, who for a twelvemonth drank thereof. And still it flowed, and flows still to this day, and mothers in whose breasts the milk is dry seek the rock of Skadar to nurse their babes at the breast of the unhappy Rosanda.

And when this ill deed was done, Vukashin departed from Skadar, but his brother Uglesha remained to hold the fortress. And himself, he went up and down throughout the land, seeking by crafty words and treacherous to turn the hearts of his people against their Tsar. And many cities he gave into the keeping of those who served him, and because of the will of Dushan none might gainsay his command.

So the seven years of his stewardship went by, and when the eighth year dawned, he ruled in all the broad domains south of the mountains of Shar, nor delivered up his heritage unto Urosh. And for our sins, God the Father ordained that the son of Dushan should be a gentle youth, sweet with the graces of holiness, but unversed in the power of the sword, who dared not punish his unfaithful servant. Yet he summoned to Kossovo Field Vukashin the King and his brother, the Despot Uglesha, hoping vainly by fair words to win from them what they would yield neither through fear of the Lord nor the dead Tsar's curse. And they parleyed from dawn to dark, and from dark to dawn, but their words were dust in the wind.

 RE they three white-winged swans that have alighted on Kossovo's green plain, or are they snow-mounds left behind by winter to greet the spring? No swans are they, for swans long since would have spread their wings in flight; nor are they snow-mounds for what snow could live under the summer sun? Nay, they are three white tents, pitched near the five domes of Grachanitsa, and one is the tent of Vukashin, King of Prilep, and one is the tent of his brother, the Despot Uglesha, and one is the tent of Urosh, son of Dushan. And these three were enemies each of the other, yea, for Uglesha coveted fiercely his brother's might. Yet, for the hopes and fears that moved them, they hid their hearts, and smiled and kissed each one the other between his black brows. But secretly by night each sent his messenger to walled Prizren, where dwelt the Protopope Nedyelko, he who had blest the last hours of Dushan and heard his dying words.

For Urosh thought in his heart: "Surely Nedyelko will declare before all the people that the empire shall be mine."

And Vukashin thought: "The priest will fear my vengeance and declare that the empire shall be mine."

And Uglesha thought: "The people scorn Urosh and hate Vukashin, wherefore Nedyelko will declare that the empire shall be mine."

Now the three messengers came together before the dwelling of the Protopope Nedyelko, and smote the door with their plaited whips and cried: "Come forth, thou Protopope Nedyelko! for thou didst bless the last hours of Dushan and hear his dying words! And thou art summoned to Kossovo Plain to declare to the Princes which of them all he named to be his heir."

And Nedyelko came forth out of the white church and cried: "Hear me, ye messengers of the mighty! Truly did I minister to the dying Dushan, absolving him of sin. Yet of his empire we spoke no word, nor of aught concerning his earthly treasure, since God hath no care for these trappings of the flesh. But if ye would summon to Kossovo Plain one who knew all the will of Tsar Dushan and can reveal it plainly, then summon Marko Kralyevitch from Prilep. Scribe was he to the Tsar, and now is keeper of the ancient books and master of their secrets, and he will speak truth with the fear of God upon him, for he fears none beside."

So the messengers journeyed to Prilep, and Marko came forth from his castle to give them greeting, together with his mother Yevrosima.

"God's benison upon you, my children! Is it well with the Tsar, and my father the King, and mine uncle, the Despot Uglesha?"

"Well are they in health but sick in spirit, Lord

141

Marko, for each would wrest the empire unto himself, though they hide their hearts and kiss each one the other between his black brows. Wherefore we are come to summon thee to Kossovo Plain, for thou art keeper of the ancient books and canst reveal which of the princes was destined by Dushan to be his heir."

Now Marko, hearing their words, ordered the ancient books of the land to be brought, and Sharatz, his piebald steed, lover of red wine and wiser than a hundred men. And he hung the books on the saddle-bow of Sharatz, and Yevrosima, laying her hands on his head, blessed her son's journey, saying: "That the milk wherewith I suckled thee be not accurst, Marko my son, bear no false witness to pleasure either thy father or thine uncle. But speak truly, though thou lose thy head thereby, for thus to lose thy head is to save thy soul."

And he answered: "Without thy counsel I had spoken truth, my mother, yet thy words will sweeten it on my tongue."

And four vessels of wine were brought, and three were such as a thirsty man might drain on a summer's day, and these Marko gave to the messengers. But the fourth was such as might have held the waters of Ochrid, and half he gave to Sharatz who, drinking, grew blood-red to the ears; and half he drank himself and, drinking, grew blood-red to the eyes. Then with a loud cry, leaping astride his steed, dragon rode forth upon dragon to Kossovo Plain.

And when King Vuskashin saw who was come to reveal the will of Dushan, he laughed aloud in his joy, for he thought: "Surely Marko will say that the empire shall be mine, for from the father it will descend to the son."

And Uglesha thought: "Surely Marko will say that the empire shall be mine, for like a fair golden apple I nourished him in my bosom. But his father was ever rude and harsh of tongue, and Marko loves him not."

And Urosh thought: "Two vultures spread their wings betwixt me and the sun, and the third comes to join them."

But Marko paused neither before the white tent of his father, nor before his uncle's tent, neither paused nor spoke any word till he was come to the tent of the young Urosh, where he dismounted from Sharatz and entered in.

And presently the sweet bells pealed forth the summons to morning prayer, and with bowed heads the Princes followed each one the other into domed Grachanitsa and, having prayed the Lord to forgive their sins, they came forth again and sat them down at tables before the church, and drank red wine and rakia.

Then Marko laid on the table the ancient books that he had brought on the saddle-bow of Sharatz, and read therefrom how the great Stefan Nemanya had, out of many zhupas, created the one land of Serbia, and ere he died bequeathed it to his son, Stefan first-crowned by his brother, the holy Sava; and how from that day it had passed in an unbroken line from father to son and from brother to brother Nemanya, each proving himself a worthy lord, extending the borders of his

143

realm and winning glory for his name and crown; but how of them all the mightiest was Dushan, first Tsar of the Serbs, the Bulgars and the Greeks.

And when he had read, Marko closed the books and smote his hand upon the table that the boards groaned and cried: "Whereof then do ye dispute, my lords? Art thou belike the son of Dushan, my father, or thou, mine uncle Uglesha? Well know ye he begot one only son who sits beside you. Are your lands too small, that by the sin of treachery ye seek to increase them? May they grow dry as the desert ere from the Tsar's son ye wrest one city that is his! Here in the ancient books the law stands clear—from the father his kingdom shall go down to the child—but though no word thereof had been written down, still should I stand before you and proclaim Urosh his father's heir, for so with his dying breath did Dushan proclaim him, naming thee, my father, for thou wert high in his trust, steward for seven years. But now the eighth year dawns, and the time is ripe to account for thy stewardship. Wilt thou have it said to our shame that the trust was betrayed?"

And Vukashin, enraged that his son should so upbraid him, leaped from his seat, and drawing the jeweled dagger from his girdle, rushed on the Prince. But Marko recoiled from the blow, and since it ill beseems a son to grapple with his father, fled from before him toward white Grachanitsa and Vukashin followed after. Thrice they circled the church, and Vukashin's breath was hot on the neck of Marko, but now from the holy place a voice spoke, saying: "Take

refuge within my walls, Kralyevitch Marko! Save thy father from the sin of slaying thee!" And Marko fled through the open door that closed behind him, and Vukashin, blind with wrath, plunged his dagger into the sacred wood. And lo! the red blood ran down.

And he cried in fear: "Alas, O God, I have slain mine own son Marko!"

But a voice spake from within the church, saying: "Not Marko hast thou slain, O Vukashin, but an angel of the Lord!"

Then did Vukashin curse his son with a threefold curse, crying: "May thy seed wither in thy body, my son Marko! May thy body never find a grave! May thy soul never leave thy body till the foot of the Turkish Sultan be planted on thy throat!"

But the spirit of the mighty Dushan, being near for the sake of his son Urosh, cried: "For the judgment thou hast spoken this day, may God reward thee! May thy face shine in the council-chamber, may thy sword conquer in battle, may thy memory be dear to thy people beyond all others while Serbia shall endure!"

And if ye would learn how Vukashin's curse and the blessing of Tsar Dushan were fulfilled on the head of Kralyevitch Marko, hear ye my tale to the end.

ET think not that Vukashin took heed of the judgment of Marko nor the ancient law of the realm for, being born to evil, what he held he held, and what lay in the hand of Urosh he plotted how to seize. Till at length the nobles, assembled in council together in the church of the holy Mihailo above Prizren, where the bones of Dushan lay buried, called upon him to yield up the empire to the Tsar. And some were moved thereto by love of Urosh, but more by hatred of Vukashin.

And when he was come before them, they cried: "We charge thee by the dust of Dushan, that cries without rest beneath these stones for the wrongs of his line, that thou restore his empire to his seed and peace to his soul."

And he answered: "Wherefore should I yield up the empire that the Tsar gave into my hand?"

And they said: "For seven years he gave it in sacred trust, bidding thee yield it up to his son when, with the eighth year, he should have reached man's stature and the wisdom of a man."

But Vukashin flouted them, crying: "Since he hath

reached man's stature, let him take what is his. What is mine I will not give."

And because they feared him, and because there dwelt no amity among them but strife and discord, as in the days before our father Nemanya, their wrath availed naught against him. So for many years confusion reigned, and none was master, and Murat, lord of the Turks, pressed ever onward into Christian lands, and Christian peoples trembled within their cities like beasts in a cage. And the Grecian Tsar, seeing that he had bidden into his house a devouring serpent, cried now upon the Serbs to join their strength to his, that together they might crush out its life. But there was none to heed his cry.

Vukashin, unto whom may the Lord render justice, bought warriors from the Magyar King, by whose aid he thought to seize those citadels still under the hand of Urosh and, having seized them, crown himself Tsar of the realm. And he had pledged Uglesha his deepest oath that, being Tsar, he would name his brother King.

So they girded up their loins to wickedness, but God cried them nay. For the stench of the blood spilled between brother and brother was grown foul in His nostrils, and His patience with our people was at an end. And He suffered the Turks to leave their city of Yedren and cross the Maritsa, setting unhallowed foot on our fatherland.

147

And when word of this evil had been brought to Vukashin, he cried: "It is well. For this army I have gathered shall first drive the invader from the land, then win it for me." And he sent messengers to Uglesha and to all his vassals, commanding them to meet him with their forces on the meadows of Chermen, westward of the Maritsa. And himself he led his army out of Skoplie by the ancient road, and came after many days to the place he had appointed.

Now Vukashin had sent runners before him to learn how the enemy was encamped, and ere long they returned with happy tidings to their lord, for they had ridden to the shores of the Maritsa, nor found any trace of the foot of man or beast.

And he looked on his shining ranks that gladdened all the plain, and laughed in the pride of his heart that was heedless of peril. And he cried: "The tidings were false that came to us in Skoplie, and the Turk dare not match himself against us. Wherefore let us feast this night, my children, and on the morrow we will cross the Maritsa, and storm the walls of Yedren." And his soldiers loosed their armor and their steeds, and the red wine flowed, and the still night rang with their cries.

But Shahin, who commanded the Turks, had led his host to the south, and far below Yedren he had crossed the river, and lay hidden in the wilderness. And because the fame of Vukashin's army was gone before him like the sound of battle trumpets, he sent one in the dark of the moon to spy out their numbers. Swiftly his courier stole toward the tents of the Serbs, and

148

the din of their revelry smote his ears from afar. And he dropped with his belly to earth, that he might escape the sentinels' vigilance, but the sentinels made merry with their comrades, nor kept the watch. And when the Turk drew nigh the campfires, he beheld by their golden flame a wondrous sight. For here was no dread host, drawn up on the eve of battle to sow terror and death, but a band of revelers who had drunk so deep of the wine-cup that many lay already in heavy slumber, while those who waked emptied their beakers anew and lifted their voices in song and ribaldry. And the war-steeds, eased of their trappings, grazed hard by.

Then swiftly he sped back to his master's tent and told his tale, and Shahin heard and rejoiced, and sent his troops straightway to the attack.

And when they were come to the Meadows of Chermen, the fires burned low and the army of Vukashin lay sunk in dreams. And as a herd of wolves on a slumbering sheepcote, so with wild cries did the heathen horde fall on the Serbs at Maritsa, to our unending shame let it be told, and slaughter them. For our warriors, torn from the very depths of sleep by fierce battle-cries and the neighing of steeds in fright, and enfolded still in the fumes of rosy wine, knew not friend from foe. Nor might they find their armor to gird it on, nor their steeds to mount them. Wherefore they drew sword and smote unheeding, and many left living by the Turk were slain by their brethren. And their steeds galloped in frenzy across the plain, trampling their masters underfoot, and the earth was hot with

149

blood, and the Maritsa choked with the bodies of heroes slain.

And when at dawn the remnant saw what havoc had been wrought among them, madness laid hold on them, and they fled from before the Turks, who followed in hot pursuit and so encompassed them about that only in the waters of the Maritsa might they find refuge. And many cast themselves on her bosom but, being borne down by wounds or their armor's weight, sank to the depths. And many, pausing ere they plunged, were overtaken by the enemy and struck down. And of the mighty multitude that had assembled on the Meadows of Chermen, only a handful left them.

But where were the lords of the host, they that with high arrogance, but lacking the blessing of God, had thought to drive the Turks out of the land? Where were Vukashin the King, and the Despot Uglesha?

Dire their fate, as presently ye shall hear. For when Uglesha saw that the day was lost, by stealth and cunning he won his way from the field, and his servant Nikola followed after him. And they rode in bitter haste for many leagues till they came, when the sun was high, to a green valley watered by a mountain stream. And Uglesha cried: "Go down and fetch me water from yonder stream, that I may quench my thirst."

But Nikola answered: "Thy golden chalice is left behind, my lord, and there is naught wherein I may fetch thee water from the stream."

150

So the Despot Uglesha dismounted from his steed, and giving his war-mace into his servant's keeping, went to the shore of the stream and knelt to drink. And as he bent his head above the water, the chain of gold that encircled his neck swung free, and the sun's rays drew fire from its heart. Then did the servant Nikola lust madly after the golden chain of Uglesha, and he stole upon him, and with the war-mace given into his keeping smote him so sore a blow that his head was shattered, and his life was spilt upon the waters. And Nikola took the chain from his neck, and left him to the beasts and the fowl of the air.

Thus, in the hour of his death, was the will of Goyko fulfilled on his brother Uglesha.

But Vukashin fought more fiercely than all his warriors, dealing and suffering grievous wounds, till there came one, lofty of stature and fresh as though new risen from his couch, whose richly wrought apparel proclaimed him Prince. And he cried: "Art thou Vukashin the King?"

And he answered: "I am."

"Shahin Pasha am I, and I have sworn to slay thee, King Vukashin. Wherefore let us fight."

And they fought. But the arm of Vukashin was weak, by reason of the wounds that oppressed him and the blood that blinded his eyes, and slowly he gave ground till he stood upon the brink of the Maritsa. And though he yielded not, but strove still to reach the breast of his enemy, he strove in vain, for with one mighty blow the Turk disarmed him and hurled him from his steed into the waters.

And many beheld how the Maritsa plucked Vukashin from among his fellows and bore him on her bosom beyond their sight, but whether living or dead they knew not. And for long years thereafter it was told how Vukashin perished in the waters of the Maritsa.

O THROUGH the breach rent in our ancient walls by the folly of our masters the Turks entered in, and like a sea whose tide might not be stemmed, they spread over all Makedon to the Vardar stream. And those who but now had striven in hatred with each other forsook their strife, speeding swiftly to the city of Urosh, that together they might take counsel how to defend their people from the oncoming foe. But in Skoplie the great bells tolled from the church-towers, for the Tsar had closed his eyes, blinded with much weeping, and laid his weary head on the bosom of God.

Thus did the mighty tree of the Nemanyas, having put forth its last weak shoot, perish from our midst, and there was no Tsar in Serbia and no son of Tsars to be raised to his father's place. And many princes clamored before the Sabor to be named sovereign, pledging their strength to free our soil of the Turks, but two there were whom our people loved beyond all others, and one was Lazar, son of Pribatz, lord now in Rudnik; yet dearer still than Lazar to their hearts was the mighty hero, Kralyevitch Marko.

153

To the golden hall of Dushan came Marko Kralye-vitch and Prince Lazar to hear the Sabor's decree. And Yefrem the Patriarch rose up from his place and spoke to them in this wise: "My sons, long have we sat in council, praying for the grace of God to enlighten our judgment and make plain the way of wisdom. For Princes are ye both, and men of might and worthy to be rulers over your land. But God hath said: 'Let Lazar be first among you, since the curse of Vukashin lies upon his son, and with his death the line will reach its end. But Lazar hath already three stalwart sons, into whose hearts the blessèd blood of the Nemanyas hath passed through Militsa, their mother.' Where-fore let Marko rule still in Prilep, bestowed upon his father by Dushan, but Lazar and his children and his children's children shall hold sway over all the domains north of the mountains of Shar. And when he hath freed our holy soil of the Turk, he shall be crowned Tsar!"

And Marko, bowing unto the will of the Sabor, be-took himself to Prilep. And for many years he held his white city against the enemy's onslaughts, beating them back again and yet again from her very gates. But his warriors perished on the walls, and none came in their stead to his aid, for all the roads and all the waterways were fallen to the Turk.

And at length Marko spoke unto Sharatz, saying: "Of no avail to struggle longer, my Shara, since one man alone, though he boast a matchless steed, may not hold a city against these sons of darkness. Moreover, we are destined to pay them tribute by the curse my

154

father laid on me at Grachanitsa. Wherefore let us do swiftly this deed we are loath to do, bearing high our heads, for if we honor ourselves, who shall dishonor us?"

Then Sharatz laid his head on the shoulder of Marko, and Marko laid his head on the neck of his steed, and they wept salt tears. And their tears being shed, they opened the gates of Prilep to the Turk, and Marko sealed with him a covenant that he should still be lord of his white city, paying unto the Sultan yearly tribute of grain and honey and the skin of beasts, and a hundred days of service in the field against whatsoever power should menace him, save the Serbs alone.

Would I might sing unto you, O Serbian hearts, of the deeds of Marko! feared by the Turks as they feared no man beside. Woe unto him who entered unbidden the gates of Prilep, for he came not forth again with a whole head! Yet these are songs for a happier day, and now ye shall hear only the tale of Marko and the vendor of merchandise in the camp of the Sultan Murat.

It chanced one day that Murat lay encamped with a hundred thousand warriors on Maritsa's shore, and through the camp a merchant hawked a sword. But though many thronged about him, coveting its beauty, there was none to buy. For it was a blade wrought of Damascus steel, and its hilts were three, and three

155

me to thy dwelling. And say to him that I have three belts of gold, and one I will give to thee and one to him and one to thy mother, if ye serve me truly and well. And if God heal me of my wounds, your guerdon shall be worthy of a prince.'

"And the maid, my sister, came unto me, and told me all that the knight had bade her say, and I descended to the brink of the Maritsa to bear him homeward. But when mine eyes alighted on the blade that hung by his side, I was filled with joy, for it was a blade wrought of Damascus steel, and its hilts were three, and three bright jewels gleamed in each golden hilt, and I knew its worth to be more than the worth of three cities. Wherefore, unmindful of my sister's tears, I wrested the sword from his grasp, and smote therewith his head from his white shoulders, and gave his carcass to the waters of the Maritsa."

And Marko cried: " 'Twas well and bravely done. But say, thou valiant slayer of dead men, canst thou measure words as well as gold and jewels? For here are three names graven upon the blade. Canst thou read them, Turk?"

"Nay, mock me not. I am a merchant trafficking for gold, and know naught of words."

"Then come, I will read them to thee. The first is the name of NOVAK, who forged the sword; the second is the name of VUKASHIN, the mighty King for whom in the day of his glory the sword was wrought; the third is the name of MARKO, son of that King, for whom in after years he destined the sword. Strangely indeed is it come at length to the hand where it should

158

rest, for I am that Marko whose name is graven thereon."

And hearing these words, the merchant fell at the feet of Marko, crying: "Pity, Lord Marko, for my sister's sake, who showed thy father kindness! Pity, for she will weep to know her brother slain!"

But Marko answered: "My gold will dry her tears. And thou shalt have such pity as thou didst give!" So saying, he smote the Turk between the shoulders, making of one man two, and cast him into the Maritsa and cried: "Go! Bear my father company!"

And gathering up his gold, he returned again to the camp, where the soldiers hailed him, crying: "God aid thee, Marko! Where hast thou left the merchant?"

And Marko answered: "He hath fared farther, comrades. Yea, with the gold I paid him for the sword he will journey even to the sea."

Thus did the son avenge his father's slaughter, knowing not that the Turk was but a weapon in the hand of God, Who at the hour of his death fulfilled on Vukashin the will of his brother Goyko.

Now Makedon wept beneath the shadow of the Crescent, but from the realms north of the mountains of Shar Lazar held the Turk by the strength of his right arm, and the help of God and his Serbian warriors. And the heart of his kingdom lay in Krushevatz, where he abode with the Lady Militsa and all his court, and men named him Tsar, though he might as she slept, and her beauty inflamed him and he lusted for the pleasures of her chaste flesh. And spreading his wings, he descended into the valley, and the fiery rain of his feathers scattered the sheep and awakened Zora from slumber. And she would have sped away, yet he suffered her not, but held her to earth and took his will of her. And when his desire had been slaked, he laid in peace his head on her white breast, that was like an apple orchard where fruits ripen and birds sing in the sunlight.

"And he lay with her till darkness shadowed the valley, then rose and embraced her, saying: 'If a daughter be born of our love, she shall be a mountain Veela; if a son, he shall be a hero to vanquish dragons and lead the hosts of a prince and slay a Tsar. Yet to none shalt thou reveal who hath sired thy child, but shalt bear him hither, and lay him beneath the branches of a pine and go thy way. And for thee, take comfort that thy fledgling shall forsake the humble valley for the glory of the mountaintop.'

"So saying, he soared aloft, and Zora lifted up her eyes and followed his flight till he vanished behind a cloud. And when she could see him no longer, she gathered her flock about her and drove them homeward, and the tears bedewed her white cheeks.

"And each morning she led her flock to pasture on the mountain slope, and she sat among them like a star among wandering clouds, but her hands were still. And ever and again she lifted her eyes to the heavens, but no Zmai flew down; and the tears bedewed her

white cheeks. Yet to none did she reveal her heart, nor tell of the child that grew within her womb.

"And at length her time was come upon her, and in the valley of their love she bare a son to her dragonlord. And she folded about him the shift of fair linen, wrought in scarlet and gold, that she had destined for her bridal bed, and laid him beneath the branches of a pine. And with a flowering spray she shielded his eyes from the rays of the rising sun and went her way, casting backward many a glance upon the valley till it was lost to her sight.

"And I saw the child where he lay beneath the pine, and his limbs were as of hewn marble, and his eyes were the eyes of an eagle that knows no fear. And presently he lifted up his voice and wept for hunger, but alas! there was none to suckle him or give him comfort.

"Now the mountain Veelas had bathed in their cloud-ringed pool and, clasping white hands, had danced the kolo, while the kind sun shed his warmth over their rosy bodies and tresses of gold. And weary at length of play, they descended into the valley to drink cool wine and rest in the shade of its trees. And as they made merry with laughter and sweet singing, suddenly the Veela Erosalya cried: 'Peace, my sisters! For I have heard the cry of a thing new-born, a lamb lost from his flock or a babe from his mother.' And they were silent, and faintly to their ears came the cry of a thing new-born that wept for hunger.

"And they flung away their shining beakers, and followed after their sister Erosalya, who found the weep-

163

ing babe beneath the pine. And cradling him in the warmth of her white wings, she cried: 'This is a hero's child and shall be ours. Who sired him I know not, but he was borne by Zora, the shepherd maid, for her shift enfolds him. He shall be reared as befits a Veela's son, and when he is grown, we will give him a steed of might and a keen-edged sword to be his servants, and he shall lead brave men in battle and wed with the daughter of a prince. Go now, and bring me hither some beast to suckle him, that his cries may be stilled.'

"And they went, and found a mare with her new-born foal, and brought them to Erosalya, and the mare suckled babe and foal till their cries were stilled.

"And the Veela Ravyola said: 'Let him be called Cobilitch, for that he hath been fed on mare's milk.'

"But Erosalya answered: 'Not Cobilitch shall he be called, lest fools should taunt him, but Milosh Obilitch, and men shall name him as they name a happy day.' So, spreading their wings, they bore to the mountain-top babe, mare and foal, and vanished in the forest from my sight."

And being well pleased with the tale of Zora, the moon forgave sweet Danitsa her fault, and kissed her white brow and left the morning sky to those who ruled it.

And Zora's babe was suckled by the mare, that he grew in strength and beauty, and the foal, his brother, bore him whithersoever he would go, and the Veelas taught him the arts of peace and war; how to speed an arrow from the bow to pierce the flying eagle's heart, how to wield the mace and the battle-axe, and how to parry blows with the wolf and by a single stroke of the sword make of one beast two. And they taught him to sing, and in their magic circle to dance the kolo, and to play music sweeter than the music of the King's guslar. And they taught him the ways of service, for he who cannot obey cannot command.

And when he was grown to be a comely youth, it chanced one day that he labored in the wilderness. And Prince Lazar, riding far afield, entered into a forest whose face he knew not, but whose trees thrust their proud heads into the sky as though they would speak with God. And in a clearing he espied a youth who felled the trees, each at a single blow, then, being weary, drove his stout axe deep into the heart of an ancient oak, and laid him down to slumber beneath its shadow. And Lazar drew nigh unto the youth, and marveled to see how the branches above him rose and fell with his breathing. And leaning from his steed, he sought to dislodge the axe from its resting-place but his strength availed not. Whereupon he alighted, and seized the haft between his hero's hands, and bent his hero's body to the task, striving to draw it forth. Yet, though the blood streamed from his hands and the sweat from his brow, he moved the axe no farther than it might have been moved by a finger's weight. Then he awakened the slumbering youth and questioned him, saying: "How art thou called and what is thy father's line?"

And he answered: "Milosh Obilitch am I called, and my mother herded sheep in the valley. But who sired me I know not, neither his name nor rank nor his deeds of valor, nor aught that a son should know of the father that got him."

And Lazar said: "Draw forth the axe from the tree," and Milosh drew it forth with his right hand and cast it at Lazar's feet.

Then Lazar cried: "By thy words and thy bearing and the might that stirs in thy limbs, thou art fruit of an eagle's loins. Wilt thou lose thy days in the forest, felling trees, or wilt thou bear a sword and serve a prince?"

And Milosh answered: "I will bear a sword and serve thee till my days are done."

And hardly had he uttered these words when Erosalya and her sisters appeared before him, and she led by the bridle a black steed of Arabia that was shod in silver, and his trappings were of jeweled silks, and his mane was braided with pearls like a damsel's tresses. And as a proud maid goes among her suitors he went, and laid his head in love on the shoulder of Milosh.

And the Veela Ravyola bore a sword of Damascus steel, thrice hilted in pearls, and its weight was equal to the weight of three heroes' swords; and the Veela Persida a shirt of cloth of gold, about whose throat a golden viper lay coiled, and its eye was a ruby of such splendor that he who wore the shirt need bear no candle to light him to the chamber of his bride. And

166

many other gifts they proffered of weapons and armor and a scarlet cloak, and when they had clad him in glory, and girded the sword about him, and bound the scarlet cloak upon his shoulders, they bade him farewell. And Erosalya gave him wise counsel, saying: "Brave be thy heart as thine outward bearing, Milosh, for the victory is given not to the shining arms but to the dauntless spirit." And kissing their white hands, he leaped to his steed and followed after Lazar to Krushevatz.

Thus did Milosh Obilitch enter into the service of Prince Lazar, and all the court acclaimed him, for he was a hero to rejoice the hearts of heroes. And the maiden Vukosava, last-born of Lazar and the lovely Militsa, looked kindly upon him; and these two pledged him brotherhood, Ivan Kossanchitch, fair as a golden tower, and Toplitsa Milan, taller than a tall tree. Only Vuk Brankovitch, heir to a hundred princes, scorned Milosh that he knew not his father, and hated him for the love that Lazar bore him.

And when he had served a twelvemonth, Lazar named him voyevoda over all his hosts, and gave him in marriage the hand of the maiden Vukosava. And bells were rung in the streets of white Krushevatz, and banners streamed from the towered walls by day and torches flamed by night, and the people rejoiced, for on each was bestowed a golden dinar from the coffers of the Prince, and a suckling lamb from his flock. And from far and near came guests, bearing kingly gifts, and one came unbidden to the wedding of his son, yea, the Zmai of Yastrebatz, who folded himself in darkness and sat among them. And of all he beheld, naught pleased him so well as the beauty of the Lady Militsa.

So for three days they made merry, and on the evening of the third day, Yefrem the Patriach and threescore priests joined in the bonds of wedlock Milosh, the Veelas' son, with Vukosava, Princess in Serbia, and brought them to the bridal chamber, and blessed the bed of their union, crying: "Be thou fruitful, thou marriage bed, whereon these two shall lie in love together."

And Milosh knew his bride and found her fair.

ND naught troubled the peace of Lazar, for he had gained a glorious victory over the Turks on the river Sitnitsa, falling with such fury upon them that only the chieftain and those who guarded him escaped unharmed. Wherefore he built in thanksgiving the church of Ravanitsa, not as many are wont to do, by the tears of the widowed and fatherless, but with the gold that lay in his treasure-house. And he took repose from battle, giving his nights to feasting and his days to the pleasure of the chase.

And returning one day from the forest as evening drew her veil over the sky, he sat him down to feast at the laden board, and Militsa sat beside him. And the gentle image of Jesus looked down upon them, bearing in his left hand the Holy Book and in his right a blessing.

And Lazar ate with joy of the savory food, for the chase had sharpened his hunger, but Militsa laid her white hands upon her knee, nor ate of the food, nor questioned her lord as to the spoils he had taken, but care shadowed her brow as a cloud shadows the smile of a radiant meadow.

And Lazar marked her heaviness, and spoke to her, saying: "Militsa, my dove, my dear one, what grief afflicts thee? Art thou not content with thy lot? Have we not broad lands and rich treasure and a castle twice walled to withstand the assaults of the foe? Are we not dowered with the crown of the mighty Nemanyas, and blessed with brave sons and comely daughters? What dost thou crave, my wife, that thy beauty is dimmed? Speak fearlessly to thy lord."

"Alas, my husband, naught do I crave, yet my heart labors beneath a grievous burden, and though I am loath to bring thee sorrow, let be done what must be done. Know then, that when last night the young moon walked in midheaven, there flew through my casement the Zmai of Yastrebatz, and unbound his wings, and doffed his cloak of flame, and embraced me, caressing my round breasts and speaking words of love into mine ear. And though I strove to thrust him from me, I might not, for his strength was greater than mine."

Then a storm broke and raged in the breast of Lazar, and leaping to his feet, he cried: "I will seek him out and slay him, and I will trample his wings beneath my feet, and cast his cloak of flame into Morava's waters."

But Militsa stayed him, crying, "Alas, my Prince, what avails thy wrath against one born of a Veela? If thou challenge him to combat, he will surely slay thee, and wherein shall thy death comfort me? Nay, I have wiser counsel, if thou wilt but heed me. When the young moon rises again, he will return and I will question him and learn who his master may be. Him shalt

thou summon from whatever far corner of the earth
he may inhabit, to do battle with the Zmai, and thus
shall we prevail over our enemy. I pray thee, my lord,
if ever I have found favor in thy sight, give ear to my
plea nor imperil thy dear life."

And Lazar yielded and bade her do according to her
will.

And when the young moon walked again in midheaven, the crown of Yastrebatz burst into living fire,
and forth from its midst the Zmai flew to the tower
of the Lady Militsa. And he entered by the casement
into her chamber, and unbound his wings and doffed
his cloak of flame, and she smiled softly upon him.
Then he embraced her, caressing her round breasts, and
whispered words of love into her ear, and at length
she said: "Fair art thou beyond measure, thou burning
Zmai, and bold as thou art fair. For were Lazar to
learn of thy coming, he would surely slay thee."

"How should he slay me, seeing I am born of a
Veela and no mortal may prevail against me?"

"And is there none indeed in all the world save God
whom thou dost fear?"

Then he gazed darkly upon her, crying: "For what
ill purpose dost thou question me?"

And she answered: "For none, else let God smite me
now in thine arms. Yet I cannot choose but marvel
at thine exceeding strength and only to please my
fancy I questioned thee, if the Lord in His might have
fashioned another hero who is thy peer."

"Since in kindness thou dost ask, in kindness will
I answer thee. In all the world there is none I fear

171

save God and the Zmai who dwells in the valley of Shagdan and is named Zmai Despot Vuk. Sworn brethren are we, for together on Yastrebatz we learned of the clouds their swiftness, and their strength of the rocks. Yet when we measured our might, grappling one with the other, ever he proved himself the victor and flung me to earth though I strove with all my arts against him. Were the Zmai Despot Vuk to challenge me, I should tremble before him, for the Lord hath endowed him with gifts greater than mine."

And when the lovely Danitsa appeared in the sky to proclaim the birth of day, the Zmai of Yastrebatz donned his cloak of flame, and bound his wings to his shoulders and flew forth from the casement, and the crown of Yastrebatz burst into living fire and he vanished within. But Militsa sought out Lazar in his tower and all that the Zmai had revealed to her in the night, she told him again.

Then Lazar wrote a letter, and struck the plume into his arm, drawing forth blood, and with his blood he sealed the seal. And he laid the letter beneath his falcon's wing and bade him bear it to the valley of Shagdan, where dwelt Zmai Despot Vuk. And the falcon flew through the white day and the night, and when he came to the place, he uttered a loud cry and let fall the letter of Lazar from beneath his wing. And the Zmai came forth, and saw the letter sealed with Lazar's blood, and broke the seal and read: "If so be thou art a righteous Zmai and a God-fearing, I, Lazar of Serbia, summon thee to do combat with the Zmai of Yastrebatz who hath injured me, having

172

entered into the chamber of my wife and forced her to his will. And if thou heed my summons, I will give thee nine charges of treasure and thou shalt rule over the kingdom of Sirmia till thy days be done."

Now the Zmai Despot Vuk pondered in sorrow the words of Lazar, for great was the love he bore his ancient comrade and loath was he to harm him. Nor was he moved by the gift of treasure and lands, but by hatred of the deed that reeked in the nostrils of God. Wherefore the true-believing Zmai Despot Vuk girded his sword upon him and saddled his black steed, and to one saddle-bag he made fast his tent and to the other three huge casks of wine, and so he set forth on the road to Krushevatz and reached her silver wheat-fields ere darkness came down. And dismounting, he thrust his spear into the earth and bound upon it the reins of his black steed, then he pitched his tent, and having drained a cask of its red wine, he laid him down to sleep.

And Militsa, greeting the dawn from her white tower, beheld in the wheatfield the tent of an unknown knight, and his black steed tethered to a spear. And she cried to her servant: "Hasten to the tower of my lord and entreat him hither!" And when he was come, she pointed out to him the tent and the tethered steed. And they gazed on the wonder, knowing not if it were a portent of good or evil, and as they gazed, a knight issued forth from the tent and raised a huge cask from the earth and drained it dry. Then Militsa cried: "Surely it is the Zmai Despot Vuk, for he drinks

173

as a hero drinks, and his bearing is as the bearing of the youth who comes to me at night."

And Lazar sent his servant to the Zmai, bidding him welcome, and entreating him to enter into the castle that he might partake of a feast laid in his honor. But the Zmai answered him, saying: "I may not enter into his castle whom my brother hath wronged, nor eat of his bread and meat. Here in the wheatfield will I tarry till the coming of night, and at thy hands do I require naught, save that thy lady leave wide her casement and abide in peace what shall follow."

And when night fell and the young moon walked in midheaven, the crown of Yastrebatz burst into living fire, and in the wheatfield the Zmai Despot Vuk drained his third cask of wine, and in her tower the Lady Militsa flung wide her casement. And the lord of Yastrebatz entered into her chamber, and unbound his wings, and doffed his cloak of flame and drew near his love to embrace her. But without, a voice as of a terrible archangel shattered the stillness, crying: "Thou who wouldst lie in sin with a Serbian Princess, I summon thee to thy doom!"

And terror laid hold on the limbs of the Zmai and withered them, and trembling, he donned his cloak and bound his wings to his shoulders, and he flew from the chamber high into the clouds, seeking to escape his doom. But in vain, for the Zmai Despot Vuk pursued him thither, and beneath the eyes of the fair young moon they struggled, and the mightier hero vanquished the lesser, and hurled him earthward. And as he fell, his voice came faintly like the voice of a dying falcon

174

from between his lips, and he cried: "Let every hero perish as I have perished, that puts his trust in woman!"

But the Zmai Despot Vuk pursued him to earth and stilled his faint voice, smiting at a single blow his head from his shoulders, and having slain his brother, he lay beside him and mourned him through the night. And at daybreak he took the head, and bore it through the gates of Krushevatz and laid it at Lazar's feet, crying: "Behold, I have brought thee the head of thine enemy!"

And Lazar answered: "Praise be thine for this deed, and the blessing of God! and nine charges of treasure, according to my word, and the kingdom of Sirmia to rule till thy days be done."

But the Zmai Despot Vuk made answer to Lazar, saying: "I called him brother whom thou didst call thy foe, and slew him at God's bidding, but I will take from thee neither land nor treasure in payment of his death."

And he went from the Prince's presence to the silver wheatfield, and mounting his black steed, he returned to the valley of Shagdan where he lived till his days were done and prayed for the soul of the Zmai of Yastrebatz, his brother whom he had slain.

**B**UT that which saddened the heart of the Zmai Despot Vuk made Lazar glad, and on the Holy Sabbath he betook himself with his knights and servitors to the church of Lazaritsa, there to bow his head in thanksgiving before God's altar for the death of his enemy. And having praised His name, he returned again in the midst of his retinue to white Krushevatz.

And he took his place at the head of the golden sofra, with the noble Prince, Vuk Brankovitch, at his left, and at his right, old Yug Bogdan, and about him in the order of their worth sat his lesser knights. And Lazar cried: "Let us honor the Lord's Day, my children, set aside by Him neither for toil nor bloodshed, but that we may savor His peace and rejoice in His blessings. Wherefore, having offered up our hearts in thanksgiving, let us now comfort our bodies with the flesh of His beasts, and the fruit of His bursting vineyards."

And mead and rakia and red wine were brought, and a golden platter, borne high on the hands of eight servingmen, was laid before the Prince, and it held the carcass of a wild boar slain by Milosh. And his comrades lifted their beakers in his praise, but Vuk

176

Brankovitch, raising the cup to his lips, tasted not of the wine.

And as they ate and drank, suddenly through the casement a gray falcon flew to the hand of Lazar, and bowing his head three times before the Prince, he cried: "Joy unending be thine, glorious Lazar, and triumph over all thy foes as thou hast triumphed over the Zmai of Yastrebatz. Yet what hath wrought thee good hath wrought us ill, and the guilt is thine. We were at peace, I and my brethren, on the mountain of Yastre- batz, that the Lord gave us to be our dwelling-place, as He hath given thee white Krushevatz. We ate of the food He sent us, and slept in the green branches of His trees, and each morning we gathered by the pool to drink and make merry, spraying our wings till they shone like the wings of peacocks. And we knew no fear, for the Zmai was our shield against dragons and every evil thing that breathes in the dark caves of Yas- trebatz. But alas! our Zmai, may God have pity on his soul, offended a prince, and now the dragon Ahzdaya hath seized our pool and poisoned its waters with his venom, and swallows at a gulp each bird or beast that approaches its brink unaware. And we may neither drink nor spray our wings nor frolic in the sunlight, and our throats are parched for thirst, and our hearts for sorrow. Now say, great Lazar, to whom shall we make moan? The Veela lingers on the mountaintop in the arms of her love, and Kralyevitch Marko, that hero who was wont to right all wrongs, drinks in Turkish taverns and whets his sword for the heads of Murat's

177

foe, while Serbia's woes go unavenged. Last night I bewailed our plight in the tall pine-tree, while my comrades hearkened and wept, but the raven cried: 'Will ye slay the dragon with weeping or drive him forth from the pool with your salt tears? Though the mountain Veela hath forsaken us, and Marko Kralyevitch rides with the Turk, yet in white Krushevatz dwells many a goodly knight, who might make an end to the dragon Ahzdaya, had he but the will thereto.' So I am come, O Serbia's golden crown, to seek justice at thy hands, and a champion to do what long since the Zmai had done, hadst thou spared him to live."

And Lazar answered: "Wise and true are thy words, O gray bird falcon, and I weep with thee in thy sorrow. And if thou wilt but forgive me thy master's death for the sin he sinned against me, thou shalt have not a single champion, but all this goodly company to do battle with the dragon Ahzdaya. What say ye, my children? Is this not a task meet for God's Holy Day?"

And right gladly did his knights pledge themselves to the combat, setting forth straightway for Yastrebatz. And on Lazar's right hand rode Vuk Brankovitch, and Milosh on his left, and the falcon rode on his shoulder to point the way.

Now in her tower the Lady Militsa sat with her daughters and gazed over the fields. And she beheld the company of heroes with silver spears and gaily prancing steeds, a sight to make glad the heart of a woman. And she marked her well-loved Lazar in their midst, and those who rode on his either hand, and she said: "Happy are ye, my daughters, in your lords. See

178

where they go beside your father, two soaring eagles, and which is the more noble to look upon no man may say."

But the proud Mara, Brankovitch's lady, answered: "How canst thou say so, my mother! Shall the son of a line only less glorious than the line of the mighty Nemanyas be named with the bastard of a shepherd maid and the nursling of a mare!"

Then anger flamed hot in the breast of Vukosava, and she cried: "Bravely hast thou spoken, sister. Yet the mare may leap high over the head of the wolf, and with her iron hoofs shatter his teeth!"

And Mara rose up and struck the white cheek of her sister, and the jewel of her finger wounded the tender flesh, that the blood ran down. And Vukosava fled from the tower, seeking refuge in the gardens below, and beneath a cherry-tree she wept for the blow she had suffered, but more bitterly still for the taunting of her lord.

And Mara laughed to see her sister's tears, but Militsa said: "Better to weep with the wise than to laugh with the fool, my child. He that does ill shall suffer greater ill, wherefore go seek thy sister in the garden, and pray that she forgive thee thine offense."

But Mara smiled a smile of scorn and answered: "Let her grant forgiveness to her base-born lord. I have no need of it."

And Militsa, seeing that she might not soften her heart, fell silent and spoke no more.

O THE pool on the mountain of Yastrebatz came Lazar and his knights, and saw a wonder. For a deer, that had wandered in far places and knew not of his peril, had paused at the water's edge to slake his thirst. And the dragon Ahzdaya, stealing upon him, had swallowed at a gulp his hinder parts, but the antlers he might not swallow. And he beat his head against the earth, striving to dislodge his prey, who gazed in anguish from his captor's throat.

And the falcon cried: "Good fortune attends you, ye men of Lazar, and the Lord is your aid. For He hath thrust a deer in the dragon's throat to be your shield, and if now ye cannot put an end to him, then call yourselves plowers of earth or merchants or keepers of the sheep, but heroes ye are not!" And he called to his brethren, who came like a thick cloud from their hiding places, to behold the slaughter of the dragon Ahzdaya.

Then Lazar cried: "Who will set free the deer?" And all his warriors raised their spears in token of their readiness for the task, but the lot fell upon Vuk Brankovitch.

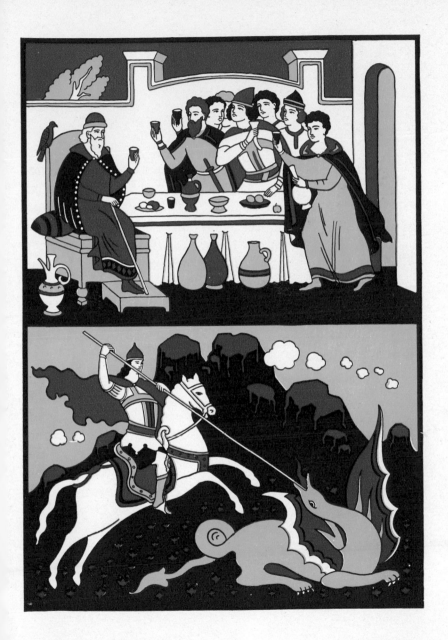

And he cast from him his sword and spear, crying: "By my mace alone and the strength of my naked arm will I slay this dragon!" But he is a fool who boasts of the deed undone, for when he had descended to the pool where the dragon Ahzdaya still beat his head against earth, he lifted high his brazen mace, and dealt him so fierce a blow that the weapon was sundered in twain, yet he harmed not the dragon but only wakened the vermin that slept in his scales. And being unarmed, he might not strike again, but must needs return crestfallen to his fellows.

And the birds in the branches made mock of him, crying: "By the strength of thy naked arm hast thou shattered thy mace, O mighty Vuk Brankovitch!"

And again the lot was cast and fell upon Milosh, who hurled his spear as he galloped to the edge of the pool, but the monster seized it between his talons, crushing it into many silver fragments. Then Milosh drew rein beside him, and raised his sword aloft, and being angered, smote with such power that the fearsome Ahzdaya was cleft asunder, as though he had been the rotting branch of a tree. And the deer, released from his fangs, sought to flee to the forest, but the dragon's head lay heavily on his shoulders, and he might neither bear it away nor cast it from him. And Milosh laughed to see his plight, and cried: "Fear not, my gentle one, but stand quietly, and I will rid thee of this head whereof thou hast no need, for thine own is fairer."

And the deer stood quietly till he had been freed of the head, then fled away, and Milosh bore it in triumph to the feet of Lazar. And the birds in the branches acclaimed him, crying: "Hail, Milosh! Praise to thy name on the mountain, praise in the valley, praise on the tongue of bird and beast while the sun shall endure!" And his comrades paid him honor, and Lazar kissed him upon either cheek, and Vuk Brankovitch gave him fair words, though envy lay coiled in his breast like an adder biding its time to strike. And with songs and wingèd spirits they took their way to Krushevatz.

Now each lady, as was her wont, came forth to welcome her lord at the castle gate, and to hold the reins of his steed as he dismounted. But there was none to welcome Milosh, and when the Lady Militsa had given her white hand to Lazar, she would have done her daughter's service to her son. But he suffered her not, saying: "My love for thy kindness, sweet mother, yet what is due the husband from his wife thou canst not give me," and dismounting, he went in quest of Vukosava, and found her beneath the cherry-tree.

And he said: "Thou hast wronged me, Vukosava. Is it meet that he who bears the battle trophy alone shall lack welcome?" And she turned her fair face to her lord, and he saw that it was ravaged with much weeping, and he cried: "What is thy sorrow? And whence this blood that stains the whiteness of thy cheek?"

And she answered: "Because the Lady Mara taunted me with thy birth, I cried out upon her, and these are the marks of her fingers on my cheek. Yet I weep not for the blow, my lord, but for the affront she hath put upon thee, for whether thou be bastard or prince, nobly

182

or meanly born, I love thee dearer than mine own black eyes." And she wept afresh.

Then the brow of Milosh grew dark, and he strode from the garden, and came upon Vuk Brankovitch where he walked in the court with the Lady Mara. And pausing before them, he cried: "Thy lady hath a forkèd tongue and thorny fingers, Vuk Brankovitch. Let her beware, lest the lamb she stings be guarded by a lion!"

Then Brankovitch, torn by the hungering wolves of hatred, cried aloud: "Here is a wonder! Look well upon him, Mara, for never again shalt thou behold a lion that hath been fed on mare's milk!"

And Milosh smote him to earth, that the stones of the court rang with his fall, but Brankovitch rose again, and the gore dripped from his mouth, and he charged as a bull, blinded by rage, that plunges and leaps and roars, yet sees not for madness the thing he would destroy. And Milosh seized him anew in his iron arms and flung him anew to earth, and would surely have slain him, had not Lazar the Prince, hearing the sounds of strife and his daughter's clamor, hastened into the court and sternly bade him hold his hand. "Are ye mad," he cried, "that ye sow the seeds of discord within my household? Our foes are plentiful as the grass-blades in the field. If ye would brawl, go brawl with Turks and split the skulls of infidels, but for my Serbian heads, I have need of them, sound and untouched of passion. Well hath it been said that where the devil cannot work a mischief, he sends a woman. But what have ye, warriors and men of reason, to do with women's wrangling? Think shame unto yourselves, my sons, that like heedless children ye have fallen upon each other, and be at peace!"

And Milosh answered: "I should have slain him, sire, and veiled his lady's bright beauty in robes of darkness and brought low her pride. But since thou wilt have it so, I put aside my wrath and proffer in friendship the hand I raised in bitterness against him."

And Brankovitch laid his hand on the hand of Milosh, saying: "Shameful is it in the sight of man, and a sin before God when brothers quarrel. Wherefore I pray thy pardon for my rash words, and take in friendship the hand thou hast proffered me."

Thus did they seal their peace under the eyes of Lazar and all his court, but within his breast Vuk Brankovitch swore vengeance by his mother's soul on Milosh Obilitch who had dishonored him.

AIN would I tarry with you, my children, among these tales of Zmai and Veela, as one who tarries overlong in a pleasant place, dreading the weary road that lies before him. Yet in the end he must take up his staff and fare forth from light into darkness.

For what man shall turn from his path marked out by God? Not you nor I nor our good Prince Lazar, in whose ears rang once more the blast of Murat's battle-trumpets, but newly stilled. And his heart was oppressed with foreboding, and long he pondered how he might silence forever that uneasy sound.

And at length, when the way had been made clear unto him, he called together the Sabor, and spoke these words: "In older days the Bulgars were our foe, and the tribes of the Magyar lands, and the Grecian Tsar, and our fathers chastened them when too boldly they set foot beyond their borders. But now I beseech you, my people, let us forsake these ancient enmities, and swear eternal faith with all Christian kings that henceforth our swords shall be keen for none save the Turk. Our single strength will not prevail against him since, like some many-headed monster, he falls but to rise again.

Yet if the sons of Christ, bound in brotherhood together, should raise His holy banner, and march from
the four corners of the earth to ensnare this monster,
what power could save him from the death that is his
due and our deliverance?"

And Lazar's words moved the Sabor to his will, and
he sent his messengers to all right-believing monarchs,
calling upon them to arm themselves for the Lord. But
Satan, who was the friend of Murat, bore him to a high
hill, whence he beheld our prince's messengers riding
from Krushevatz to the four corners of the earth to
kindle the flame of war against him. And he cried:
"Lord Allah, let not the Christians unite, else am I
undone!"

And Satan whispered in his ear: "Do thou smite
first."

And again Prince Lazar called the Sabor together,
for his messengers were returned to Krushevatz with
tidings of cheer. And these were their tidings: "The
flame is kindled, and the sons of Christ will add their
strength to ours, marching from the four corners of
the earth to destroy the Turk, when thou, O Prince,
shalt sound the battle call!"

But even as they gave tongue unto their joy, the
guard who kept watch at the castle gate entered in
haste, and knelt before Prince Lazar and cried: "One
who rides in the train of Murat, the Turkish lord, stands
at the gate with a greeting to thee from his master."

And as a storm blast quenches the light of a torch, leaving all in darkness, so did the naming of Murat quench gladness in the hearts of those who heard it, and laughter on their lips. And Lazar cried: "Let him be brought before me."

And the messenger of the Sultan entered in, and laid a parchment upon Lazar's knee, and he broke the seal, and read: "To Prince Lazar the Serb, in his city of Krushevatz, this poisoned draft from Murat, lord of the Turks. Know, thou Lazar, that dost call thyself ruler in Serbia, never hath there been nor ever shall there be one land and two masters, one slave and two fealties. Wherefore do thou deliver up to me the golden keys of thy city and thy son Stefan, and do thou pay me tribute for seven years. And if thou wilt not, then meet me on the field of Kossovo, whither I lead three hundred thousand men, and with sabers we will apportion the land."

And Lazar's cheek grew pale and faint his soul, as he read before the Sabor the letter of his enemy, but when he had made an end, he cried: "Ye have heard the words of the Turkish chieftain, my hawks. What is your answer? Shall we pay him tribute, or give him battle on Kossovo for our fatherland?"

And as with one voice they answered: "Let us give battle."

Then Lazar turned to Murat's messenger, standing with proud arms folded upon his breast, and spoke in this wise: "Say to thy lord: he who calls himself ruler in Serbia will neither deliver up to thee the keys of his city nor his son Stefan, nor will he pay thee tribute. But he will come to meet thee on Kossovo, and drive thee by God's will out of his land."

But when the messenger was departed, the Prince leaned his head on his white hand, and from his eyes streamed tears like rain. And the grief of Lazar smote also the hearts of his nobles, who sat in silence about him and in heaviness of soul.

Then Milosh rose to his feet, and gazed for a space in wonder upon his comrades, then broke into speech: "Wherefore do these words of Murat, my lords, cause you such pain as though a serpent, rising from their midst, had spat venom into your mouths?"

And Vuk Brankovitch, turning his face to the Prince, made answer thus: "A fool may be dowered with valor, but wisdom is the heritage of kings. The Turk leads three hundred thousand men against us, and though we summon aid from Bosnia and the mountains of Zeta and the country of the Arna-uts, yet, having mustered all who owe thee service, thy numbers will be scarce a third of the foe's. Shall one Serb vanquish three Turks? Fight and die we may, but conquer we shall not, and our blood will be spilt in vain. Wherefore I counsel thee, great Lazar, yield up thy city and thy son Stefan unto the Turk, and pay him tribute, nor send thy people to perish on Kossovo Field."

And the eyes of Milosh blazed as though fire had been kindled in their depths, and he cried: "Better to die in glory than live in shame. Better to perish on Kossovo Field, my well-belovèd Prince, than that our children and our children's children should call down

the curse of God upon our heads who sold them into bondage!"

And the nobles flocked about him, crying: "Milosh hath spoken well."

"Yea, and I would speak further, my lord. Who hath heard save from the Turk himself what his power may be? Therefore let Ivan Kossanchitch, knowing their tongue, steal through their battle line. Let his eyes measure their numbers, let his ears give heed to their speech, whether it be the speech of slaves or heroes, and let him bring true tidings of all that his eyes have seen and his ears heard. Meanwhile, we will draw up our strength in Krushevatz, the while swift couriers hasten through the land, bidding thy vassals and voyevodas gather their troops to the uttermost man, and ride at their head to Kossovo. Then let us go forth together against the Turk, and thou shalt judge if we be an army of babes to flinch before their menace, or of strong fighters fit to encounter, aye, great Prince, and to vanquish the mightiest foe."

Now when Milosh had spoken, he knelt at the feet of Lazar to hear his reply, but Lazar raised him from the ground, saying: "Kneel not before me, Milosh, for thy words have shamed me, but according as thou hast counseled, let all be done."

Then Vuk Brankovitch stepped forth from among his fellows, crying: "I bow to thy will, my father, and beg leave of thee to depart straightway for Prishtina, where twelve thousand chosen warriors await my command. None will fight more fiercely, Lazar, and on whatsoever day thou shalt appoint, I will ride at their head to meet thee on Kossovo." And when Lazar had appointed the day, Vuk Brankovitch went forth from the council-chamber and made ready to depart for Prishtina.

And presently Ivan Kossanchitch, appareled as a Turk in green and scarlet, and girt with a shining silver scimitar, returned again to the Prince, that he might bless his journey for a happy end. And Lazar blessed him, and kissed him on either cheek, saying: "Go with God, my son."

And Milosh awaited him beside his steed, standing eager at the castle gate, and spoke softly, saying: "Thou who art dearer to me than a dear brother, if thou perish, Milosh will weep for thee. But if thou return in safety through the Turkish lines, I charge thee bring me thy tidings ere thou reveal them to another."

And Ivan answered: "That will I, brother-in-God," and so departed. But behind the gates the false Vuk Brankovitch, preparing to set forth, overheard their words, and they watered the evil seed in his evil heart.

Now those who dwelt hard by white Krushevatz returned each one to his stronghold to marshal his troops, and Milosh arrayed the army of the Prince, that numbered forty thousand. And from the castle Lazar's swift couriers took each his way—one to the golden-bearded lord of Zeta and one to Ban Turtko of Bosnia; one to Musa, chieftain over the wild Arna-uts and one to Musitch Stefan in Maydan, his tall city; one to Pavle Orlovitch and one to young Laucha, he of the wonder-sword that might neither be broken nor consumed in flame; to these and others rode the couriers of Lazar the Prince, and the words of his message were in their mouths: "Let him that is a Serb, born of the seed of Serbs by a Serbian mother, come at the dawning of the fifteenth day hereafter with his power to Kossovo, that together we may go forth against Murat and drive him by God's will out of our land. But he that will not come, may neither maid nor man-child bless his dwelling, may the sound of mirth be stilled beneath his roof and the dancing of the kolo before his threshold; may naught thrive under his hand, neither the lowing kine in his meadows, nor the vineyard upon his hills, nor his silver wheatfields, but may all be eaten up as with rust."

And to those who heard, it was as though the voice of the mother of God had spoken, and they made vow unto Lazar's messengers that they would come on the appointed day with their power to Kossovo.

On the seventh day thereafter, ere the sun had opened his golden eye in the heavens, Milosh went forth on the road to Kossovo to meet, if so be it were the will of God, his brother Ivan returning from the Turkish tents. And truly, having ridden for an hour, he beheld him from afar, and spurred on his steed, that blue flame leaped from his nostrils and yellow flame from his hoofs. And meeting on the road to Kossovo, they spread wide their arms and kissed each one the other upon his cheek.

And Milosh said: "Hast thou measured the Turkish

host, Ivan my brother? What sayest thou of their numbers and their valor? Shall we overthrow them with ease on Kossovo, or with travail and the shedding of much blood?"

And Ivan answered: "Milosh, my brother, thine ears will be loath to hear what my tongue must speak. From the height of Vranyevo I beheld the Turkish host, and their white tents covered the earth like a fall of snow, and their banners were a cloud that hid the sun, and their lances a dark forest where no bird might fly. And having beheld them thus, I went down from Vranyevo and entered the camp, and passed thrice through their lines, being challenged of none. From Izvor to Uvor I rode, and from Uvor to the Marble Stone, and from the Marble Stone to the waters of the Sitnitsa. Then what shall I tell thee, Milosh, save the truth, bitter though it be in the blood? The Turks are numbered as the leaves of the trees, and pride sits on their brows. In shining white are they clad, and in green and scarlet, and the trappings of their steeds are of gold and silver, and their sabers are bright with many fiery jewels. Hero to hero they stand, and steed to steed, so thick that should God send the rain to fall on Kossovo, no spot of earth would be left bare to receive it. Were we as many grains of salt, my brother, as we are Serbs, still should we be too few to salt their meat. Nay, not with ease shall we overcome this foe, but with travail and with terror and with rivers of blood. Wherefore I pray thee, let me be the first to give my life, as I have been first to carry tidings of evil."

"Who shall be first lies hidden in the hand of God.

192

But as for thee, having served thy people well, thou canst better thy service. Hear me, Ivan. Bear not this tale to the Prince, lest his heart misgive him for the sake of those who must perish, and he march into battle not as a master of men, but as their shepherd, dreading the fangs of the wolf. Then say to Lazar that the Turkish hosts are worthy of combat, yet not to be matched in strength or numbers or valor with our dauntless Serbs. Say to him, they are an army not of tried warriors, but of merchants and artisans, fighting neither for the love they bear their monarch nor for lust of battle, but for ducats to buy them bread. Say that at every post their sentinels stand guard in terror of our approach, and like a wind from heaven we shall descend upon them, sowing destruction and death. Hearing these things, Lazar will laugh, and our people will take heart from his laughter, and so they will go rejoicing to their task, and not in dread of defeat. This is the counsel I give thee. Wilt thou turn aside from the truth to follow it?"

"Thy wisdom is greater than mine, and I am content to do thy bidding, Milosh."

So, giving rein to their steeds, they galloped to Krushevatz where Lazar awaited them. And they entered into his presence, and Ivan knelt before him and kissed his white hand, but Milosh stood apart. And Lazar said: "What are thy tidings, my son?"

And he answered: "Thrice have I passed through the Turkish lines, my lord, being challenged of none. From Izvor to Uvor I rode, and from Uvor to the Marble Stone, and from the Marble Stone to the waters of the Sitnitsa, and I say to thee that this foe is worthy of combat, yet not to be matched in strength or numbers or valor with our dauntless Serbs. They are an army, not of tried warriors, but of merchants and artisans, fighting neither for the love they bear their monarch nor for lust of battle, but for ducats to buy them bread. At every post their sentinels stand guard in terror of our approach, and like a wind from heaven we shall descend upon them, sowing destruction and death. These are my tidings, as God hath been my guide."

Now when he had heard these words, Lazar laughed from his full throat and cried aloud: "Then in God's name, let us be about this task that He hath appointed us. Our troops stand ready. Our kinsmen await us before Kossovo. With the dawn we will set forth. Do thou, Ivan, my good and faithful servant, seek rest between labor and labor, and do thou, Milosh, take command, and let thy voice be in all things as mine own."

And there sounded ere long in the streets of Krushevatz the clang of armor and the neighing of steeds and the lamentations of women, for now was the husband torn from the breast of his wife, and the son from his mother, and the youth from the arms of his belovèd.

And Lazar entered into the chamber of Militsa and spoke to her, saying: "I would lie with thee, my wife, for who knows what night will look again on our love?" And they lay together, and took comfort each from the other and were at peace.

And Lazar said: "With the morrow's dawn we set forth for Kossovo Field to smite the Turk. And with me thy father rides, old Yug Bogdan, and thy nine stalwart brothers, and with me ride my servants and all my household. And thou shalt remain alone."

And she answered: "God's blessing go with thee, my husband, and with my father and my nine dear brothers, and with all thy host. Yet, being alone, whom shall I send to bring me word of the battle, and bear my greeting to thee and thine to me? Thou hast many thousands, my lord, to fight with thee, and if in thy train there ride more or less by one, wilt thou be the poorer? Wherefore I pray thee, by the love I bear thee, leave me not friendless, but out of my nine brothers give me one to share my vigil."

"Say then, which of thy brothers wilt thou choose to stand beside thee?"

"I will choose Boshko Yugovitch, for he is gentle and will not deny his sister when her heart cries to him."

And Lazar drew from his finger a golden ring and gave it to Militsa, saying: "Take thou this ring, my heart, and before the dawn, go forth with thy maidens to the city gate where the troops will pass. And when thou shalt see approach thy gentle brother, Boshko Yugovitch, he that doth bear my standard, show him Lazar's ring, and say to him that he shall give the standard into whose hand he will and stay beside thee."

And Militsa took the ring from her husband's hand and laid it in her bosom.

And before the dawn, she went forth with her maidens to the city gate and took there her stand. And lo! a wonder! for the black earth trembled and shook, and there came into sight the glory of Lazar's hosts, their banners rising and falling like the waves of the sea, their golden lances striving to pierce the heavens, their steeds flying so swiftly toward Kossovo that is was as though they were borne not by mortal beasts, but on the wings of the wind.

And now she beheld the sacred banner of Lazar upheld in the hand of Boshko Yugovitch. Of emerald silk was it fashioned, and the golden cross of the Lord was emblazoned upon it, and the golden apple of the kingdom of Serbia; and tassels of gold hung from its corners, caressing the shoulders of Boshko Yugovitch and the neck of his golden steed. And he looked neither to the right hand nor the left, but only before him.

And Militsa moved into her brother's path, and laid hold on his steed, and the steed knew the touch of her hand and was quieted. And she drew forth the ring from her bosom, and spoke to her brother, saying: "Thou gentlest of my brothers, Boshko Yugovitch, with this ring hath Lazar pledged thee to my service. For being alone, whom shall I send to bring me word of the battle, and bear my greetings to my lord, and his to me? But he hath many thousands to fight with him, and if in his train there ride more or less by one, will he be the poorer? Wherefore I pray thee, heed the cry of my heart, and give thy standard into whose hand thou wilt and stay beside me."

And the gentle Boshko unlearned his gentleness, and cried in anger: "I will not stay beside thee, nor give my standard into another's hand, not for the ring of Lazar nor for all his shining city of Krushevatz. Shall

my comrades say: 'Behold the coward Boshko! he that
watched with the women, and bartered his sword for
Militsa's white tower, leaving his fellows to shed their
blood on Kossovo for the Cross!' Nay, if thou must
have a messenger, give thy ring to Damyan, for he is
the youngest and fairest of us all and a dove in his
mother's breast. And so farewell." And setting spurs
to his steed, he galloped through the city gate.

And now she sees her seven brothers riding, straight
and proud in the saddle, but straighter and prouder
than all is he who rides in their midst, old Yug Bogdan.
And she clasps her white hands in entreaty and calls on
their names, yet they look neither to the right nor
the left but only before them, and gallop through the
city gate.

And after them followed Damyan, the youngest and
fairest of her brothers, and his face was the face of a
child that laughs in the sunlight. And he led the
Prince's swan-white battle-charger, bridled in silver
and saddled in cloth of gold, that snorted and reared
and pawed the earth with his hoofs, scenting the fray
from afar.

And Damyan looked both to the right and the
left, and saw his sister, and checking his steed, he
cried: "Behold me, Militsa! It is thy brother who leads
the Prince's war-charger to battle. Am I not brave to
look upon?"

And he drew near and bent his brow to her lips,
and she laid her white hand upon his shoulder and
whispered to him: "Brave art thou to look upon, Damyan, and the heart of thy sister faints for need of thee.

197

Have compassion with me, for lo! I am alone, and whom shall I send to bring me word of the battle, and who will comfort me if my people perish? I pray thee, my brother, by the Prince's ring, that I hold from him as a pledge, do thou give his war-steed into whose hand thou wilt and stay beside me."

And Damyan cried: "What folly dost thou speak? Where hast thou heard, thou daughter and wife of heroes, that a hero should forsake his comrades? I would not stay beside thee, nor give the steed into another's keeping, though an angel of God should bar my way, crying: 'The Lord commands it.' And now begone from our path, lest we trample thee beneath our feet for these thy words." And he flung her from him, and galloped through the city gate.

And Militsa, undone by her griefs, lay in darkness where Damyan had flung her, and her maidens surrounded her, weeping for their lady's sorrow. And now there bore down upon them Lazar the Prince in the midst of his chieftains, Milosh at his right hand, and at his left Goluban, his faithful servant, and behind him Ivan Kossanchitch and Toplitsa Milan. And their flowing hair and their beards were tossed by the wind and mingled with the manes of their steeds, and the chieftains' kalpaks were adorned with waving plumes and with clasps of silver, and their sabers of damascene steel touched the black earth, and from their shoulders fell mantles of many colors like a field in bloom. But the Prince's kalpak was adorned with a clasp of jewels, and the hilt of his sword with many precious stones, and his mantle was one whose like no

king of these days may wear, for fifty charges of gold was the worth of the inner side, while the worth of the outer side may not be measured.

And Lazar looked on the Lady Militsa, lying among her maidens, and the tears flowed into his beard. And he spoke unto his servant Goluban, saying: "By thine oath of service I command thee, dismount from thy steed and bear my lady to her high white tower, and abide with her there and be her comforter. For many will fight with me on Kossovo, but none will remain to guard my dearest treasure. Now swear to me that thou wilt not forsake her, but cleave by her side while she hath need of thee."

And Goluban swore, though his heart spoke not as his lips, and he bore the Lady Militsa to her tower, and her maidens followed after them, but Lazar and his chieftains rode on toward Kossovo.

And when Militsa awoke in her high white tower, and beheld the faithful Goluban by her side, she cried: "What dost thou here?" And he told her all as it was befallen, and she saw that he was as one whose life blood ebbs from his veins. And she said: "Go, Goluban! I clear thee of thine oath! Do thou follow the Prince thy master. Only this do I ask at thy hands in return for the oath I have given back to thee, that if thou live, thou bring me word of the battle and of my lord, and of Yug Bogdan, my father, and my nine dear brethren. Wilt thou, Goluban?"

And he knelt and kissed her white hand and cried: "Though my spirit be torn from my body, I will not die till I have brought thee word of the battle, and of

199

thy lord and of Yug Bogdan, thy father, and thy nine dear brethren." So saying, he left her and mounted his steed and followed after Lazar to Kossovo.

And having ridden for six days, pitching their tents in the light of the evening star, the Serbian army came on the seventh day to the waters of the Sitnitsa, where their kinsmen awaited them. A braver sight shall ye never behold, my children, for there was Ban Turtko of Bosnia at the head of ten thousand, ardent and strong as flame; and Musa, chieftain over the wild Arna-uts, leading four thousand tribesmen, who joined not with their brethren but drew apart, gazing upon them from beneath eagles' brows; and young Laucha, he of the wonder-sword that may neither be broken nor consumed by fire, commanding a thousand men-at-arms; and Pavle Orlovitch with three thousand; and Ban Strahinya of the Golden Beard, in the midst of nine thousand laughing warriors, who rode from the west as Lazar rode from the north, shooting their silver arrows at the sun; and twelve thousand were under the hand of Vuk Brankovitch, foul the sound of his name in Serbian ears! And all were assembled, save only the proud host of Musitch Stefan, whose city was distant from Kossovo twelve days' journey.

And they pitched their white tents by the waters of the Sitnitsa, and the scarlet tent that was the tent of Lazar they pitched in the midst thereof. And Vuk Brankovitch went in to him, where he lay on the skin of a lion, seeking repose, and poured bane into his ear: "Sire, thy chieftain Milosh, whom thou dost love, hath betrayed thee for gold unto the Turk."

And Lazar sprang from his couch, and his brow was black and his hand was upon his sword, and he cried aloud: "May thy false words stick in thy throat and strangle thee!"

But Vuk Brankovitch answered him softly, saying: "Amen to that prayer, if my words be false, my lord. Yet hast thou marked how Milosh takes counsel alone with his two sworn brethren? And hast thou heard it told how he rode forth to meet thy messenger returning from Kossovo, that he might question him unknown to thee? And shall I tell thee how I came upon them, ere I left white Krushevatz, plotting thy downfall, sire?"

And the eyes of Lazar grew dull as the eyes of a beast that hath suffered a mortal wound, and he turned his head aside, speaking no word. And Vuk Brankovitch went out from his presence.

A FEAST was laid in the prince's tent by night, and his nobles and voyevodas were bidden to partake thereof. And Lazar sat at the head of the golden sofra, and at his right hand sat old Yug Bogdan, and at his left hand sat Vuk Brankovitch, and according to their honor and rank were his knights disposed.

And having eaten, and drunk two draughts of cool wine, Lazar took again from the hand of the cup-bearer his golden chalice, and lifting it high, he cried: "To whom shall I pledge my cup on the eve of battle? Shall I drink to length of days? Then must I drink to thee, old Yug Bogdan, father and sage. Or to noble blood? Then must I honor thee, Vuk Brankovitch. Or to those with whom I am knit most dearly in love? Then must I empty the chalice to you, my Militsa's brothers, ye soaring falcons fledged in a single nest. For beauty I must name Ivan Kossanchitch. For a hero's mien and the stature of a hero, thee, Toplitsa Milan. Yet to none of these will I drink on the battle's eve, but to him whose hero's deeds have crowned him with a crown of glory. To thee, Milosh Obilitch, do I lift my cup! Thy health do I drink, my friend and my betrayer, thou who wert true at the dawn but false ere the night fell, thou who wilt forsake me on the morrow and sell me for gold unto the Turk. Drink this pledge with me, Milosh, drink long and deep! Take the chalice in honor from the hand of thy Prince, and drain it dry!"

And Milosh leaped to his feet, and took the chalice from the hand of Lazar, and bowed to the black earth. "Praise be thine," he cried, "O glorious Lazar! Praise be thine for thy pledge and for thy chalice, yet none for the evil charge thou hast laid against me. No traitor am I, neither at dawn nor nightfall, being true to thee and to the Cross we defend. But if thou wouldst know the traitor, look where he sits at thy knee, and thy robe covers him, and he smiles as he drinks cool wine, the smile of the serpent in the garden of Paradise. On Kossovo Field shalt thou learn, O Lazar, who is thy friend and who is thy betrayer, for as God is my witness, to prove to thee my faith I will slay the Sultan Murat. And if, having slain him, I am saved alive, I will bind Vuk Brankovitch to my battle-lance, and on the stones of Kossovo will I shatter his body and spill his lying blood." And having spoken, Milosh dashed the golden chalice to earth and went out from the tent of Lazar, and his two sworn brethren followed after him, leaving silence and unquietness behind. And the feast was ended, and the guests departed from the presence of their Prince.

Then Lazar laid him down, and slumber closed his weary eyes. And as he slumbered, there flew from the holy city of Jerusalem a swift gray falcon, and a swallow fluttered in his beak. Yet see, no falcon is this that alights by the waters of the Sitnitsa and enters into the scarlet tent, no falcon and no young swallow, but Elias, the man of God, who bears to the Serbian lord a letter from the Lord of All the World. And Lazar broke the seal and read: "Say now, thou child of Sava's blood, if thou wilt choose for thy heritage an earthly or a heavenly realm. For if thou choose the earthly, then shalt thou smite the Turk on the morrow, both horse and rider, and drive him out of thy land; but if the heavenly, then shalt thou surely perish by his sword, and with thee all thy host."

And Lazar held counsel with his heart, then spoke unto the Lord, saying: "Dear God, who in Thy mercy hast written a letter to Thy servant, bidding him choose between an earthly and a heavenly realm, how should I falter between these two, seeing that the kingdom of earth endures but for a day, while Thy kingdom shall endure forever. Surely I will choose the kingdom of heaven, forswearing the delights of this world and mine enemy's downfall." And when he had chosen, he fell again into peaceful slumber.

And at the hour when Danitsa bathes her face, scattering jeweled water over the earth, he awoke, and the dream was fled from his memory. And he heard the bells of Grachanitsa calling men to prayer, and he said unto his nobles: "Till the banner of Musitch Stefan appears on yonder height, we may not sound the battle-trumpets. Wherefore let us betake ourselves to the house of God, and pray in humbleness of heart for the victory ere we gird our swords upon us."

And they went forth, Lazar and all his knights, to Grachanitsa, yet three there were who rode not by his side but far behind him, and they were Milosh Obilitch and his two sworn brethren, Kossanchitch and Milan. And when the steed of the Prince had outstripped their steeds by many spear-lengths, they turned their course and galloped toward the enemies' tents.

And crossing the waters of the Sitnitsa as the day grew bright, lo! the Turkish camp lay spread before them in all its splendor, even as Ivan Kossanchitch had beheld it. And three sentinels barred their way.

Then Ivan spoke to them in the tongue of their fathers, saying: "We seek audience with Murat the Sultan." And one departed to bear this word to his lord, but two remained to keep the watch.

And he that was departed sped to where the Sultan's tent, crowned by the sun and moon, stood in the midst of Kossovo, flaunting its banners to the wind. And he entered in, bowing thrice to the earth, and cried: "Three Serbian chieftains, like three shining dragons, seek audience with the Chosen of Lord Allah."

And Murat cried: "Return to them again, and inquire at their mouths if they be come to yield themselves to our will, or to bid us defiance. And bind to thy lance three standards, of white, of scarlet and of emerald. If the Serbs be ours, thrust thy weapon aloft for all to see, but if they deny us, then shalt thou take captive those shining dragons and bring them before me."

And the sentinel bound the standards to his lance, and returning to the edge of the camp, he cried to the

Serbs: "Are ye come to yield yourselves up to the will of our lord, or to bid him defiance?"

And Milosh replied: "We are come to yield, as the wind yields itself up to the will of the waves, and the hawk to the sparrow's will."

But Ivan, speaking the words again in the tongue of the Turk, that he might know their meaning, said: "We are come to yield," and said no more.

And the sentinel thrust aloft his lance for all to see, and the Turkish warriors thrust aloft their lances in reply, shouting in token of their joy. And their ranks parted, leaving clear a path whereon our Serbs galloped to the Sultan's tent.

But Milosh alone alighted from his steed, and when Murat's slave would have taken the reins from his hand, he suffered him not, giving the steed into the hand of Kossanchitch, while into the keeping of Toplitsa Milan he gave his battle-lance.

Now Murat sat in state on a golden divan, and the golden ring of Osman decked his finger, and so bright was the jewel thereof, that by its light be might have supped in darkness as though it had been the fullness of day. And his foot was upheld on a cushion of cloth of gold, and his councilors stood close about him.

And when Milosh drew near his throne, he cried: "Thou art honored beyond all Serbs, Milosh Obilitch, for I give thee my foot to kiss."

And Milosh bent low, yet not so low as to the Sultan's foot, and bending, plucked the dagger from his girdle and thrust it deep into the belly of Murat, crying aloud: "Honored am I above all Serbs, Osmanli,

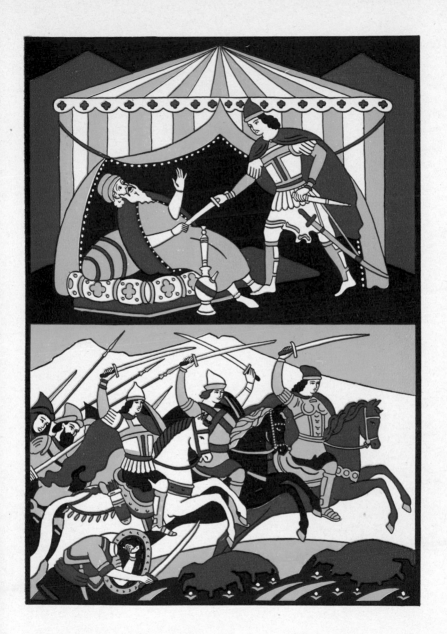

for I give thee death!" Then drawing his sword, he turned, and as a whirlwind fells the forest oaks that lie in its path, so did the sword of Milosh strike down in fury the Turks who sought to bar his way.

And he gained the portal and mounted his faithful steed, and took from the hand of Toplitsa Milan his battle-lance, and he cried: "Murat is slain, my brothers, by the hand of Lazar's betrayer, Milosh Obilitch! Now save yourselves as ye may, and if ye may not, send ere ye perish a thousand Turks to their doom, for each will be an enemy less to your lord, and a blessing upon your heads."

And now the Turkish warriors pressed upon them, as the black earth presses heavily on a seed, but as the stalk thrusts its way to the light, breaking the earth that confines it, so did these peerless heroes break through the midst of their foes to an open place, where they turned and fought.

Sweet to behold—dear God, may the praise be Thine!—were the swords that slashed, and the battle-maces that crushed, and the Turkish heads that rolled on Kossovo Field. Yea, like green grass before the sickle's sweep did they fall and die, those godless ones who plied their arms as though in some holy cause.

Yet, alas, an axe may not cut down a mountain, nor three fighters the army of a prince! And in the end one came behind Milan, and thrust a saber hilt-deep into his body, and the shining point issued forth again from his breast, red with his blood. And he turned and slew his slayer ere he fell to earth, crying: "Farewell,

207

my Milosh. Avenge thy brother, whom thou dost leave behind on Kossovo Field."

And Milosh answered: "Farewell, my brother. Soon will I follow thee."

And they two fought on, till one came behind Ivan and cleft his right arm from his shoulder. But still in his left hand he wielded the battle-mace, while the red blood poured from his wound as a mountain stream, released from the bondage of winter, pours down its slope. And he fell to earth at last, crying: "Forgive me, Milosh, that I leave thee to fight alone. May God Whom thou lovest aid thee."

And Milosh answered: "Go in peace, dear brother. Soon will I follow thee."

And now he fought alone, the matchless warrior, hero of heroes, the noble Milosh Obilitch. Alone he fought, and so hot was his rage against the Turks who had taken the life of his brothers, that with the voice of a hundred lions he bellowed, and blood gushed forth from his nostrils and his eyes and ears, and he smote not like a man but like the flail of God, laying low each one that drew nigh. And at length they drew back in terror, and none dared aproach him.

And the chieftain Balaban, who watched from a nearby hill, cried to his men: "Your blind eyes see not that which they look upon. Rider and steed are one, and till ye have sundered them, ye shall not triumph. Plunge therefore your spears into the earth, their sharpness upward, and make a ring about him, so high and wide that he may not overleap it, so dense that he may not drive his charger through. If he escape us then, no Serb is he but a fiend from the depths of hell, and vain is our labor."

And they plunged their spears into the earth, their sharpness upward, making a ring about Milosh and his steed. And when the steed beheld the glittering wall that enclosed him round about, terror maddened him, and he hurled himself upon it, but to no avail, and again and yet again, till seeing that he might in no wise hinder the steed, Milosh leaped from his back. And at length he lay with shattered legs, the hapless beast, among Turkish spears, whinneying for his lord.

And having made an end to the steed, they seized their spears again and advanced upon Milosh, awaiting them with drawn sword. The first he smote in two from neck to thigh, afoot as he was and his enemy nobly mounted, and the throat of the second he pierced with his battle-lance, and the third he thrust through the navel so swift and deep that his bowels poured forth from the wound. But now the Sultan's hosts descended upon him, and wrested sword and mace and lance from his grasp, and set him upon a charger, binding his arms behind him and his legs beneath the belly of the steed. And so they led him to the tent of the dying Murat.

And having brought him thither, they would have slain him at their monarch's feet, but he forbade them, crying: "Milosh shall die as I decree his death. But now do ye bid my sons sound the battle alarm, for I would know ere I perish who hath been destined by God to win the day."

And that ye may know what was unknown to Murat, ye shall hear how his sons dwelt not together in love, as befits the children of one house, but each was torn with hatred of the other for the deep desire he cherished to be named heir to his father's power. And Bayezid was stronger than his brother, and having learned of the Sultan's grievous wound, he summoned Yakub to his tent, saying: "Come to me, Yakub, that we may divide the command." And he sent his servant without to guard the portal, and he loosed the sturdy bowstring from his bow, and when Yakub entered, attended by his bodyguard, he smiled upon him, saying: "Dismiss thy servant, for it is not meet that another's ears should hear what passes between us. And what need hast thou of a bodyguard, since in thy brother's tent there is none to harm thee."

And Yakub could not choose but obey. And being left alone, Bayezid leaped on his brother and felled him to earth, and with the sturdy bowstring of his bow he strangled him. Then did he call the two servants within, even his own and the servant of Yakub, and from beneath heavy brows he gazed upon them and spoke: "My brother hath been slain, by whom I know not. Yet I would not have the Sultan's dying hours darkened afresh with this woe. Wherefore do ye take him and cloak his body, and lay him where none shall find him till the battle be done."

And the servant of Yakub would have opened his lips to speak but, gazing on the face of the Prince, he trembled and fell silent. And kneeling beside his

210

master, he cloaked his body, and so they raised him from the earth and bore him where none should find him till the battle was done.

Thus did it come to pass, that when Murat's messenger sought out his sons to give them his command, he found not Yakub, though he rode up and down the field in search of him. And Bayezid alone sounded the battle alarm and led the Sultan's power against the Serbs.

AZAR the Prince knelt with his nobles before the Lord in white Grachanitsa, and the holy fathers sang the liturgy, and peace abode in that place. But suddenly there burst through the wide-flung portals one who had watched by the waters of the Sitnitsa and cried aloud: "The Turks advance upon us!"

Then Lazar sprang to his feet, and called on the name of Milosh as a child in terror calls on his father's name, but Milosh answered not. And he saw that the guard had words on his tongue to speak, yet spoke them not, and he cried: "What wouldst thou say?"

"Sire, an hour is gone since Milosh, with Ivan Kossanchitch and Toplitsa Milan, passed over the waters of the Sitnitsa to the Turkish tents."

Then Lazar roused his swooning soul, and girded up the might of his fathers that slept within him, and cried to his lords: "Hear me, my children! Though the eagle's wing be maimed, who is his peer? Milosh is gone and Kossanchitch and Milan, to what end we know not, and Musitch Stefan tarries long on the road from Maydan. Yet still are we ninety thousand, and with Christ in our hearts Whose banner we defend,

212

shall we not go forward? And if we conquer, we conquer, and if we perish, we perish in the hand of God Who in death will rain such blessings upon us as, living, we may not hope to win. Wherefore to die is to live, and defeat is victory. So, courage, my lions! Back to our tents that we may divide the command and ride forth to do battle for the Cross and golden liberty!"

And they rode back, Lazar and his nobles and chieftains, to the camp by the Sitnitsa, and they arrayed their troops, each man his own. And Lazar mounted his battle-charger, placing himself at the head of the forty thousand whom Milosh was wont to command, and his right hand was guarded by Boshko Yugovitch, bearing his standard, and his left by the faithful Goluban.

And to each voyevoda save only Vuk Brankovitch he appointed a place, and to him he said: "Do thou, my son, lead thy twelve thousand faithful ones to the Chara Plain, and when thou shalt hear the trumpet sound thrice in the field, come forth from within the forest, and put an end to what we have bravely begun." And Vuk Brankowitch led his troops to the Chara Plain, while the battle alarm rang clear, and the armies of Lazar went forward to meet the Turk.

What words shall I find, finding only tears, to tell you of this battle that bore unending sorrow in its wake and glory unending! On yonder side of the Sitnitsa did they clash, Christian and unbeliever, and none can say whose blow was the first to fall, nor whether the first to perish was friend or foe. Only this we know, that our Serbs, being outnumbered, yet fought like wolves that smell the blood of the flock, smiting each man his

Turk and yet another ere he himself was slain. And Lazar led them on, exhorting them with words of cheer and mighty deeds of valor, and where the Turks were thickest, there rose the holy banner above their heads, as it were the holy countenance of God. But now an arrow struck the steed from beneath him, and Lazar fell, and one cried: "Our Prince is slain," and another took the cry from the lips of the first and, deadlier than the shafts of their enemy, did these false tidings breed havoc among the Serbs, and they turned their faces and fled.

But Lazar, mounted afresh, cried out upon them: "Whither do ye flee, my comrades? Shall I cut down the heathen single-handed?" And hearing his voice, they returned again to the charge with hearts renewed, dealing stout blow for blow. But again his steed was cut from beneath him, and in that moment a scimitar pierced the breast of Boshko Yugovitch, who fell with his standard at the Prince's feet, and again the cry was heard: "Lazar is fallen! The holy banner of Christ lies in the mire! The Turk hath vanquished us!" But Lazar snatched his standard from the earth and gave it into the hand of Goluban, and mounting the steed of Boshko, he cried: "Yet again, my hawks! Musitch Stefan rides swiftly to our aid, and within the forest bides Vuk Brankovitch, awaiting our need!" And again they rallied about him.

Then Lazar bade the trumpeter sound the call that should summon Vuk Brankovitch, and he blew three blasts that rang clear and high over the battle's din. And from the forest that borders the Chara Plain, he issued forth at the head of his troops, and galloped into the field, and the sight was as the sight of an angels' host to the eyes of the Serbs. But woe to the Serbs and woe to Lazar the Prince, and eternal woe on the soul of Vuk Brankovitch! who, having sealed a covenant with Murat for treasure and lands, tarried not beside his kinsmen, but crossed with all his power to the Turkish lines, raining death upon those he had sworn by the Cross to defend.

And when Lazar saw what thing was come to pass, he raised his arms to heaven, crying: "Now I know Thy will of me, for the dream that was fled from my memory is returned again." And he cried to his people: "Let all who will not follow me, follow Vuk Brankovitch, and share the curse I call down upon his head, and burn with him in never-ending flames! But ye that love me, however small your number, I bid you ride after me to death!"

And he spurred his steed into the midst of the field, and his people pressed behind him, and where they passed naught could be seen save the gleaming of swords, and the tossing of manes and plumes, and the flight of silver arrows, and the flowing of blood. Yea, in a sea of blood did they wade that rose to their very stirrups and their girdles, and befouled the waters of the Sitnitsa, and polluted the air of heaven with its fumes. And hour upon hour the battle raged, and they gave no care to their lives but only to slaughter. And of those that fell, the Turks outnumbered the Serbs by two to one, yet still was their living strength greater than ours.

But each day, whether of joy or sorrow, flows to its end, and the end of the day of Kossovo was at hand. For Musa fell, and young Laucha, and Ban Strahinya, and many valiant chieftains, and those who remained were wearied with much fighting, for where they struck down a Turk, it was as though two rose up again to smite them. And their hearts were sick with grief for their fallen comrades and for the treachery of Vuk Brankovitch, and their souls faltered.

And Yug Bogdan was slain in the midst of his sons who perished beside him, till only Damyan, youngest and fairest of all, was left alive. But at length his hand, wielding the sword as one that hath been tried in many battles, was severed from his wrist, and he fell beneath the feet of galloping steeds that crushed out his life.

And Lazar, bleeding from a score of wounds, as his blessèd body bears witness to this day, beheld from afar how the men of Yug Bodgan, bereft of their leader, were scattered in confusion and like to flee. And darting from beneath the hand of the Turks, he sped to overtake them, but his steed stumbled and fell into a pit that had been dug of old by peasants to snare wolves.

And there his enemy, led by the chieftain Balaban, surrounded him and drew him forth and bound him hand and foot, but his servant, who lay beside him, they left for dead.

And when they saw that their Prince had been taken, despair laid hold on our Serbs, and they fled from before the face of the Turk, who followed them in close pursuit. And many were put to the sword, and many

216

perished in the waters of the Sitnitsa, and many were taken captive. Yet, alas, my children, ye buds of Serbian soil, what need to tell you more, for well ye know that theirs was the field and the day and the victory, and ours defeat and death.

N KOSSOVO FIELD did the Turkish chieftains pay homage unto Bayezid with shouting and the blare of clarions, crying: "Hail, Bayezid! Hail, worthy son of thy sire!" And big with pride, he betook himself to the tent of Murat and knelt beside his divan, and spoke to him, saying: "Under my command hath the enemy been cut down and put to rout, and Lazar taken captive."

And Murat's soul, that had wandered between life and death, returned wholly into his body, and he said: "Where is thy brother?"

And Bayezid answered: "Dead of a mortal wound."

"May Allah guard him in death as thee in life. Thee, Bayezid, do I name heir to my lands and my power and my throne, and thou shalt be called Yilderim, for like a thunderbolt from the hand of God hast thou wrought destruction. And now let Lazar be brought before me, for it is meet that we, who shall bear each other company when we leave this earth, should once stand face to face ere we set forth."

Then Lazar was led within, and beheld his chieftain

Milosh lying bound at the feet of the dying Murat. And all that had been hidden was made clear.

And he spoke unto Milosh, saying: "Be thou blest, my son, that thou hast kept faith with thy people. But for this blaze, kindled before its time by thy rash spirit, thou shalt answer to God."

And Murat cried: "Nay, Lazar, wherefore dost thou lay on Milosh the burden, since thine was the folly to take up arms against me. And now we three lie dead, who might have savored the breath of life for many kind years."

And Lazar answered: "Better death by thy side than life beneath thy heel, O Murat!"

And as darkness descended on the Field of Kossovo, these three met death. For the head of our Prince was smitten from his shoulders, and Milosh was slain with a sword-thrust in his breast. Yet for this Thy vengeance, wrought by the Veelas' son, we thank thee, Lord! that Murat lived but to see his foemen slain, then perished in agony. And his heart was buried on Kossovo, where still it lies, but his body was borne to the tomb of his fathers in Brusa.

And Milosh was laid to rest at the feet of his lord, that he might serve him in death as in life he had served him.

EEP, my children, weep for Musitch Stefan, who drew nigh the Field only as the next day's sun drew nigh his journey's end. And he met a slender maiden, bearing on her head a ewer of bright gold, and close to her breast she clasped a knight's kalpak, woven of fine threads of silver, and adorned with pearls and the plumes of gay-winged birds. And he drew rein and spoke to the maiden, saying: "God aid thee, little sister. Whence art thou come with thy ewer of bright gold and thy silver kalpak?"

And she answered: "God aid thee, mighty voyevoda. Each day at sunrise I am wont to go to the Sitnitsa to fill my golden ewer at the stream, but this day, as I knelt by the shore, I saw that her waters ran foul with blood, and thick with the bodies of heroes and their steeds. And looking beyond, I marked on Kossovo Field many dead warriors, yet those there were who still drew breath in pain, being sorely wounded. Fearful was the sight to mine eyes, and I wept to behold it, yet I crossed the river, and filled my ewer at a spring I know of, and laved the brows of dying men, and their lips. And one said to me: 'When I am dead, take my

220

silver kalpak and cherish it, as in heaven I shall cherish
thy memory, Kossovo maid;' and when he was dead, I
laid it in my breast. And though my heart grieves for
yonder goodly youths who have perished, yet I am
young, my lord, and I cannot choose but smile when
I look on these gay plumes and flowers of pearl."

And Musitch Stefan smote his brow that the blood
ran down, crying in anguish: "May God's curse rest
upon me all my days, that I am come too late to the aid
of my Prince." And he sped onward, followed by his
warriors, to the battle's edge.

And there he beheld a sight that turned his bones to
water, for under the darkening sky Kossovo Field lay
stretched before him, hidden beneath the bodies of the
slain, and from their midst noisome vapors arose. And
thick as a shattered forest lay the broken lances of
heroes, and their blunted spears, and their swords
rusted with blood, and their scatheless arrows. And a
lonely steed mourned for the death of his master, and
the distant howling of wolves was borne through the
air, and the flapping of vultures' wings.

And Musitch Stefan cried: "Too late am I come to
fight among you, my comrades, yet not too late to bear
you company," and plucking his sword from the sheath,
he fell upon its edge and perished.

Weep, my children, shed bitter tears for the Lady
Militsa, who walked with her daughters in the gardens
of Krushevatz, awaiting word of the battle. And two

221

ravens flew from the south, lighting on her slender tower, and thrice they croaked, and thrice they flapped their wings, then spoke to one another thus: "Is this in sooth the tower of Lazar the Glorious?"

"Yea, for oft have I seen the Lady Militsa, her white hand shading her brow, watch at the casement for her lord's return from the hunt."

"Then where doth she tarry, now that we have brought her tidings from Kossovo?"

And Militsa heard their speech and cried from below: "God be with you, ye two black ravens. What tidings do ye bring me from Kossovo? Have ye seen the armies clash? Have ye marked the victor?"

And the ravens answered: "God be with us truly, Lady Militsa, for thee he hath forsaken. We have seen the armies clash, and two monarchs perish, even he that held sway over the Turkish hordes and thy well-loved husband. And few are the Turks that have outlived the battle, but fewer still the Serbs."

And as they spoke, Goluban rode through the gate, and he bore his left hand in his right, and his steed was bathed in his master's blood. And Militsa cried: "What evil thing is befallen, Goluban?"

And he strove to speak, yet his words issued like wounded birds from his mouth: "Lift me, I pray thee, from my steed, and bathe my wounds with water and my lips with wine, and seek strength to hear what I lack strength to tell."

And they lifted him from his steed, and bathed his wounds in clear water and with red wine his lips, and when his strength was revived within him, Militsa cried: "Is it well with thee now, Goluban? Canst thou tell of the battle? Hath Lazar perished indeed? And my good sire? And all my nine dear brethren? Dost thou bear tears to my daughters as to me? What of the noble Milosh and Vuk Brankovitch? Speak, Goluban, I pray thee, ere thy course be run."

And he answered: "On Kossovo Field have they perished, my sweet lady, Lazar the Glorious and all who followed him. Think not to behold them more, neither thy lord who fought like a lion, yet was snared in a pit for wolves, nor Yug Bogdan, thy father, lying dead among his sons. And for thy daughters, I bring tears and honor to one, but to the other dark shame. For Milosh Obilitch stole into Murat's tent and with his dagger slew him, bright shine the deed and long may the tale be dear to Serbian hearts! But curst be the memory of Vuk Brankovitch, and curst his seed, and curst the womb that bore him! Thy lord, proud Mara, betrayed us to the Turk! May the curse of his people lie heavy on his black soul in life and death!"

And having fulfilled his pledge, Goluban perished. But Militsa and her daughters loosed their tresses, crying upon God to comfort their bitter grief.

YEA, weep, my children, and beat your breasts for an agèd mother's sorrow! Take pity, Lord, on the mother of the Yugovitch who kneels at Thy shrine and prays: "Give me the falcon's sight and the wild swan's wings, that I may fly to Kossovo, and behold with mine eyes Yug Bogdan's nine sons, dead on the battlefield, and the tenth, their sire."

And the dear Lord wrought a marvel, and gave her the falcon's sight and the wild swan's wings. And she flew to Kossovo, and beheld with her eyes the nine sons of Yug Bogdan, dead on the battlefield, and in their midst the tenth, their sire. And beside them stood nine battle-spears in the earth, and on the spearheads nine gray falcons cried aloud their woe. But the mother's heart was hard within her, and from her eyes no tears flowed down.

And she called to the nine gray falcons, who followed after her, and they returned to her castle in Krushevatz. And from afar her sons' nine wives espied her, and came forth to welcome her, and the falcons alighted, and lo! no falcons were they, but her sons' gray steeds. And their wives wept to behold them, but

224

the mother's heart was hard within her, and from her eyes no tears flowed down.

And when the night had reached its darkest hour, she heard from his stall the cry of Damyan's steed, and she spoke to his gentle bride, saying: "Dost thou hear, O thou beloved of Damyan, the voice of his steed lifted in loud lament? Doth he hunger for the eating of white grain, or thirst for Morava's waters?"

And she answered: "Nay, my mother, neither for hunger nor thirst doth he lift up his voice, but for sorrow that his master lies on Kossovo's dark plain, as I lift up mine." And she went forth to the stall, and laid her white cheek on the neck of Damyan's steed, and wept with him. But the mother's heart was hard within her, and from her eyes no tears flowed down.

And she watched through the night at the casement, and with the dawn came two black ravens flying from the south. And their wings were bright with blood, and they bore in their talons the torn hand of a hero, on whose finger gleamed a ring of gold.

And they let fall the hand in the mother's bosom, and she drew it forth and gazed upon it, turning it from side to side. And she spoke to the gentle bride of Damyan, saying: "Dost thou know, O thou beloved of Damyan, whose hand I hold in mine?"

And she answered: "Yea, my mother, well do I know the hand, whose finger bears the ring I gave my love on the night we were wed."

And the mother gazed on the hand, turning it from side to side, and spoke softly, saying: "Thou dear hand! O thou fair young blossom! Where didst thou

225

grow and where wert thou cut down? Woe is me, within my womb didst thou grow, and on the field of Kossovo wert thou cut down ere the sun had warmed thee."

And her heart melted within her, and grew big and broke with pity for the nine sons of Yug Bogdan and the tenth, their sire.

Mourn, ye sons and daughters of your people, let the sound of your weeping fill the ears of earth and rise to heaven, for the desolation that is come over our land! Mourn for the days when Serbia bloomed like a garden, watered by the fountains of Paradise! Mourn for our wickedness that moved the Almighty One to chasten us with the scourge of the infidel! Like vultures they swooped down after Kossovo, O bitterness! and we had neither hero to defend nor king to rule nor sage to counsel us. And they seized our citadels, slaying graybeard and youth, and our maids they deflowered and our children they bore into bondage. And for want of herdsmen our cattle fell on the hillside, and for want of reapers our grain withered on its stem, loosing such famine among us as the world hath not known, and by God's mercy shall not know again. And those who escaped the sword were devoured by hunger, and those whom hunger spared fell a prey to wolves that howled at the walls and stole through the shattered gates, tearing the flesh of Christians night and day. And all good things, yea, wheat and wine and laughter, perished

226

from our midst, and those who were left in life envied the dead.

Yet not for aye shall the Lord be blind to our tears, and not for aye deaf to our supplications, by the sign He hath shown us, by the curse of Vukashin upon Marko, his son, that was God's blessing. For death may not take him, but he sleeps, our hero and hope, on the skin of a wolf in the mountain's deep-lying heart, and his sword is thrust into the living rock, and Sharatz keeps watch beside him. But day by day the sword puts forth its strength, freeing itself from the rock that holds it, and day by day the steed eats of the moss that God hath set as a dish at his faithful feet. And in that blessèd hour when the sword of Marko shall fall at last to earth, and the moss at the feet of his steed shall be consumed, he will wake from his slumber and leap to the back of Sharatz, and sword in hand, will ride forth out of the cave, shouting his battle-cry to our listening hearts. And our souls shall be cleansed of sin, and our land of the stranger, and a king shall rule once more on the throne of Dushan, and Serbia's sun, that hath gone down in darkness, shall rise again, flooding the heavens and earth with golden light! Dear God, send swiftly thy long-promised day!

227

Explanation of Serbian Words Used in the Text

Juslar: *Serbian bard*
Higumen: *churchman, head of a monastery*
Kalpak: *pointed headgear*
Kolo: *Serbian national dance* (*literally: wheel*)
Rakia: *alcoholic drink made of plums*
Sabor: *Serbian council of nobles and churchmen*
Sofra: *low table around which diners sat on cushions*
Tovar: *load carried by pack-horse*
Veela: *female spirit of forest and mountain, golden-haired and white-robed, possessing supernatural powers*
Voyevoda: *military leader*
Zhupa: *a province*
Zhupan: *ruler of a province*
Zmai: *supernatural being, part dragon, part beautiful youth, inhabiting the mountains*

TABLE OF DATES

---

330 A.D. Dedication of Constantinople (Tsarigrad) by Constantine the Great

499 Bulgarians invade Eastern Empire

518-27 First historical record of crossing of Danube by Slavonians

571 Birth of Mohammed

610 Serbs appear in the Balkan Peninsula

842-67 Reign of Michael the Drunkard in Byzantium

867-86 Reign of Basil of Makedon and beginning of Makedonian Dynasty in Eastern Empire

976-1025 Reign of Basil II (Bulgar-Slayer), direct descendant of Basil of Makedon

c.976-1025 Samuel's reign over the Bulgars

1018 Basil II destroys Bulgarian Kingdom

1170-1196 Stefan Nemanya, Grand Zhupan of Serbs

1196-1228 Reign of his son, Stefan First-Crowned

1204 Constantinople taken by Fourth Crusade

1217 Stefan is crowned first King of Serbs by Rome

1219 Sava is created first Archbishop of Serbs

1220 A.D.	Stefan is crowned first King of Serbs by Eastern Empire, discarding crown of Rome
1243-1276	Reign of Urosh, third son of Stefan First-Crowned
1261	Constantinople is retaken by Michael Paleologus
1276-1282	Reign of Dragutin, elder son of Urosh
1282-1321	Reign of Milutin (Stefan Urosh II), younger son of Urosh
1288	Osman becomes chief of Ottoman tribes
1322-1331	Reign of Stefan Urosh III, Milutin's son
1331	Defeat of Bulgarians by Serbs at Velbuzhd
1331-1355	Reign of Dushan the Mighty
1346	Dushan is crowned Tsar
1346	Emperor John Kantakuzen of the Eastern Empire asks Turks for help against Dushan
1354	Turks take Gallipoli
1355	Death of Dushan
1355-1371	Reign of Urosh and Vukashin
1359	Murat becomes Sultan
1361	Turks take Adrianople (Yedren)
1371	Battle of the Maritsa
1372-1389	Rule of Lazar
1389	Defeat of Serbs by Turks at Kossovo. Death of Lazar. Assassination of Murat
1459	Complete subjugation of Serbs by Turks
1805	Revolt led by Kara George
1815	Revolt led by Obrenovitch, resulting in Serbian emancipation from Turkey